Other Books By
SCOTT DOUGLAS VAUGHAN

The Memories of a Home Series
Stories about a small-town boy's life during the 1960s and 1970s
Brookwood Road (2014)
Elm Street (2016)
Hickory Trail (2018)

The Beauty Queen & The Reporter (2019)
A love story

www.scottdvaughan.com

Dedicated to the memory of
Terry Thompson, Director,
Jesup Recreation Department, Jesup, Georgia
who said, "Yes, you can."

And To

Mike Addy	Rhett Huffman	Jimmy Scurry
Al Beard	Robbie Joyner	Chuck Shirley
Lee Benton	Murry Kinard	Keith Stokes
James Berry	David Lance	Jimmy Terrapin
Greg Bowers	David Lewis	James Thompson
Chris Carter	Sam McCrary	Brian Thornton
Milton Clark	Jim Mabe	Jay Tompkins
Chris Davis	Bruce Mackay	Dale Warner
Pat Frawley	Mike Morales	Donnie Watts
Joel Ganger	Ed Nelson	Brad Wesson
Glenn Graves	Ronnie Nix	David White
Ricky Grice	Chris Page	Richard Whitmire
Gregg Hendrix	Bill Payne	Leslie Wiggins
Jimmy Hood	Dusty Phillips	Keith Wilks
Mike Hornacek	John Pitts	Glen Wright

Thank you for blessing my life and the lives of hundreds of boys.

I have tried to recreate events, locales, and conversations from my memories. In some instances, I have changed the names of individuals and places. I also might have changed some identifying characteristics and details such as physical properties, occupations, and places of residence. This is a memoir inspired by people, places, and events.

Some of these stories are true.
Some of these stories are based in truth.
Some of these stories should have been true.

If you want to touch the past, touch a stone.
If you want to touch the present, touch a rose.
If you want to touch the future, touch a life.

~ Unknown

PREGAME

THE SUN WAS SETTING on a warm Tuesday in February – not unusual weather for the Deep South, but just a tease of the spring that was to come in forty-five days. The robins were all over the yard, signaling spring was just around the corner. Frank Wilcox looked at his watch and saw it was 5:15 p.m. He drew a deep melancholy breath.

For the past few years, about this same time, the melancholy swept over him. At baseball fields all across Concord County, boys of all ages were climbing out of cars and trucks for baseball practice. They would have about seventy-five minutes of safe daylight, and coaches – or at least the smart ones – would have a practice plan that kept those boys engaged, moving, and learning.

"Every boy must be active," Frank said to himself, recalling his bark at the first practice each year. Usually dressed in sports pants and a sweatshirt, his eyes were hidden behind sunglasses just covered by a navy-blue hat. "If you are just standing around watching everyone else, well, you'll be doing that the rest of your lives. Be all in, boys. Be all in."

Watching the robins searching for insects in his yard, Frank Wilcox took another big, deep breath – more of a resigned sigh – something he had done all his life during contemplative moments

1

like this one. He sat on a porch swing off the back of his home. His German shepherd, Queen, lay near him and occasionally looked in his direction, waiting perhaps on a walk or for him to throw something fetch-worthy.

"Queenie," he said out loud, "it smells like baseball today."

It had been a handful of years since the scoreboard had turned off for Frank Wilcox. It happened for everyone sooner or later, or at least that's what Frank's long-time assistant coach, Richard "Doc" Holladay was fond of saying. Doc was especially fond of saying it when a local high school star finally gave up his parents' dream that he would be a Major League Baseball player.

"Did you hear the scoreboard turned off for Joe and Robin's boy?" Doc said, relaying the news to Frank. "Great boy, but couldn't carry all of that ability past puberty."

For Frank's four sons, the baseball scoreboard had turned off shortly after becoming teenagers. In high school, two of them played varsity football, another was an award-winning stage actor, and another played a year of lacrosse but generally enjoyed construction projects.

Frank got out of the swing and walked to the corner of his yard – a ghostly graveyard of old baseball equipment, scrap lumber, and worn-out tools he had planned to give his boys. He stared at the graveyard. There was an old pitchback, an inverted Y of metal tubing between which a rotten string grid remained stretched. Frank's four sons had used the pitchback for a dozen or so years, practicing their fielding. Frank had long been a believer that over a season, good defense prevailed. Hitting slumped; defense never slumped. There was also a stack of old aluminum baseball bats, and he remembered when most of them had been bought and which of his boys had used them. Almost buried in an undergrowth of cedar branches and kudzu vines, Frank noticed two old heavy-duty rubber hitting tees and a SoloHitter that allowed his boys to hit a baseball dangling from elastic bands. An old Instructoswing was turned on its side, and it made him smile. His boys hated using it because an incorrect swing through two parallel tubes often jarred hands and served as a reminder of improper technique. Covered in leaves was an old five-gallon yard bucket Frank had used for practice baseballs, punctured tennis balls, and Wiffle balls. When he removed the lid, he found a few rotten tennis balls and a cracked stop watch.

"You can't coach speed," he said out loud, remembering the draft-day advice of a fellow coach. "You better draft speed, Frank. Right now your roster looks like an offensive line." Frank went out and bought a stop watch and used it at every predraft player assessment to ensure he had speed on his roster.

Frank breathed deep and exhaled. His wife, Vicki, had been fussing about this graveyard, wanting to clean it out, haul the old baseball junk to the dump, and then reclaim this dark corner of the yard. She had visions of a shady nook, perhaps with a playhouse for grandchildren. He had postponed the inevitable and yet knew this spring would be the season when Vicki put her foot down.

Queen had followed him to the graveyard.

"I made a terrible mistake, Queenie," he said. "I should have given all of this stuff away years ago so other boys could use it. I'm too damn sentimental." He paused. "Or lazy." He smirked. "My daddy used to say the Wilcox clan is genetically lazy."

He turned back toward the house and said again, "Wow, it does smell like baseball." He sighed. "I miss it, Queenie."

3

There were no two ways about it, Frank Wilcox was in a self-ascribed funk, and the start of baseball season made it worse. His four sons were grown and gone – moved away, married, and involved in their careers. He and Vicki had four sons living in four states. Some people passed into *empty nest* very easily, embracing a season of personal revival, usually with a spouse they could date all over again. Though he loved Vicki – "my Vicki," as he called her—his empty nest transition had not been easy. He missed the noise and chaos.

At Vicki's request, he had taken his melancholy to a pastor friend, whose children were still at home. The well-intentioned man had no idea what Frank faced and quoted what Frank knew was a sentimental cliché: "View empty nest as a change rather than a loss. It's definitely the end of a certain time or a way of being together as a family. But it's not loss, because loss is when something is gone. Forever."

This funk wasn't just about empty nest.

For more than twenty years, in four different communities, Frank had coached boys in baseball, specifically boys between nine and twelve. Within those years, he had also coached his own four boys. Those twenty-plus years included competitive spring seasons and non-competitive fall seasons as well as summer and winter instruction he provided for families whose boys wanted to learn fundamentals. Full-time service for two decades becomes a lifestyle, and Frank grieved its closure.

Everyone around him knew how much he loved it all. Even his mama had quipped, "One day, Son, you are going to miss all of this." She was right. A good friend had returned from vacation and given Frank a souvenir plaque that read, "We interrupt this family for baseball season." Frank hung it over the back door of the Wilcox home. The coaching and its involvement with players and their families had become a part of Frank's identity.

He missed excited boys coming to practice, shedding hours of pent-up energy from school. He missed the feeling of a family reunion that came with each opening day at the ballpark. He missed playing early Saturday games and then staying at the ballpark all day surrounded by the community of like-minded friends. He missed four-piece chicken finger baskets from the concession stand. He missed watching a gaggle of little boys throw a tennis ball against the concession stand in a funky game they called wall ball. He missed throwing pregame batting practice in chilly February weather and then the raging heat of May and June. He missed the crazy little dugout cheers the boys sang throughout the game. He missed the times he met weak hitters or weak throwers for Saturday morning help as parents sat watching from the seats of oversized SUVs. He missed the insane stress that came with building a competitive team of nine- and ten-year-olds while not letting the stress show. He even missed the parents – even the one who still shunned him because his boy didn't make a postseason All-Star team. Frank held no grudges. He knew the disappointment shared with a son who did not make the cut for a team. He completely understood.

When the scoreboard turned off for Frank Wilcox, it was like the death of a great friend. He mourned that friend's death and even had a backyard graveyard to remind him of the passing. That he was also going through empty nest added to these feelings of loss. He was grasping in the dark, grasping for something secure, and couldn't quite find that thing to fill the time on his hands.

5

Returning to the bench swing, he sat down and gave a kick to the ground to begin the back-and-forth sway. He cursed to himself.

"Are you out here swinging or mourning?" Frank's wife, Vicki, said as she stepped out on the porch.

"It's that time of year," he said.

She sat beside him on the swing. "You could go find a team to help, Frank."

"No," he said. "It would never be the same, and that would just be disappointing."

The years he had coached baseball had taken a physical toll. He had chronic tendonitis in his throwing elbow. It was so bad he had recruited a former player – the Bird – to throw batting practice for his last two teams. It had flared horribly during his last season. Frank also had a touch of arthritis burning in both his hands. Throwing a baseball reminded him of it. He had radiating pain in his hip, presumably from standing so much during games and practices. He felt lucky just to have made it through his youngest son's final year of Pony League.

Frank kicked the ground again, creating even more lift for the swing.

"Empty nest blues," Vicki said, patting his left knee.

"I do miss our boys," Frank said. "I miss their friends. I miss all the noise. I miss the chaos. Daddy once told me that time would fly away, and it has, but I didn't expect it to be so quiet. Now I know what he meant."

"You also miss the baseball," she said.

"I do," he said.

"When the season starts, we'll go to the ballpark on Friday nights, eat chicken fingers, and sit in the outfield like we used to do," she said. "We won't know anyone, but it will be fun."

"We can do that," he said, realizing they probably would not do that. Part of the ballpark's lure was seeing hundreds of friends, visiting with them, and cheering on boys he knew – even some that played on rival teams. Most of those he knew from the ballpark had moved on as he had; there wasn't much joy going to the ballpark with a lot of strangers. It just seemed, too, that parents had unhealthy goals for their boys – they were too caught up in comparing them to the superstar kid down the street.

"You are acting like an old man," she said, cutting straight to it. "You just need to find something else to do because I'm tired of this melancholy."

"I know," he said, and he did know. He hated feeling like a pansy-ass, which is what his brother Jack would call him right now. He stared at the empty yard where the boys once played catch, had home run derbies with a Wiffle ball, practiced their pitching, or took swings on a hitting tee. He had even used Wiffle-style golf balls and a sawed-off dowel rod to help teach them focus at the plate. He imagined them playing one cat – a baseball game from Frank's childhood that could be played with only three players and two bases. He had learned how to play one cat while in Cub Scouts long ago in his hometown of Acorn, Georgia.

He always smiled, remembering a backyard altercation with his son, William, who at the time was eight.

"Down and ready!" Frank barked as he prepared to hit his sure-handed infielder a series of ground balls. On the very first one, William let it go between his legs. "Get your butt down on the ground!"

William had thrown his glove toward Frank and retorted, "My butt is on the ground. The ball hit an acorn!" Frank could not help

7

but laugh, even now. The acorns were still there. William's personality and temperament were a lot like his own.

Vicki got out of the swing and walked to the wooden shed. She opened the door, reached inside, and returned, handing her husband an old, worn baseball. Stamped on it was "Property of Frank Wilcox Baseball." The stamp seemed unusual, but practice baseballs were a hot commodity, and coaches were known to borrow or steal from one another through several seasons. Every coach marked his baseballs; Frank was the only one using a rubber stamp.

"Here, you can use this as a pacifier for your whining," she said, laughing as she walked in the house and left Frank outside.

Frank breathed in the teasing smell of spring that included the scent of fresh-cut grass from the Methodist church's parsonage across the road.

"Lord," he prayed out loud, "I hope I made a difference."

All those who invest in children make a difference.

He opened his eyes, and Queen put her front paws up on the seat of the swing. It looked like she might push him.

"It's going to be an early spring, Queenie," Frank said, pointing to the Methodist parsonage. "Preacher is already cutting his grass." He closed his eyes and thought he could hear the excited after-school chatter of boys lined up across from one another in parallel lines, warming up by playing catch.

Somewhere a coach was shouting, "Down and ready!"

As a boy, Frank Wilcox had been like many of the boys he had coached.

He loved baseball, knew a lot about it, and followed the Major Leagues, but wasn't going to be a long-term baseball player. Sure, he could catch and throw alright, but his hitting was terrible. He had gotten beaned in the face as a kid and had never gotten over it. That fear of getting thrown at eventually forced him out of playing after only three seasons between third and fifth grades.

Like many of the boys he coached, he was not athletic, could not run fast, was far too nervous-natured, and was easily distracted. He had no natural athletic ability – not one ounce.

"Where would *you* have drafted *yourself* as a kid?" Vicki asked him one night over dinner. They were talking about the league's player draft that was coming up.

"Very late," he said. "Probably sixth round or so. I might have gone fifth round because Mama was pretty good looking."

"What does that have to do with anything?" Vicki asked with a puzzled look on her face.

"It's a bunch of men sitting around a table, evaluating boys they don't know well," Frank said. "You first draft the ones you know can play – the All-Stars. Then you draft the ones that impress you at skill assessment – most likely the ones nominated for All-Stars, but didn't make it. After that, you draft the ones you know – or the ones whose parents you know. Then, you draft the friends of your sons or from families you like. And, then, well . . ."

"At the end of it, you draft the ones with pretty moms?" Vicki asked. "That's awful."

9

Frank shrugged his shoulders. It was awful, but it was what happened when a bunch of men gathered around a table, evaluating and drafting boys for a two-year team.

"Had I not been coaching, you might have gotten the boys picked a round or two early," he said, laughing. She threw a napkin at him.

"Stop talking," she said. "I don't want to hear any more."

"For the record, I was not one of those coaches."

She held up a hand to stop him from talking.

Frank's daddy, Tom, had hoped his oldest son would enjoy athletics. Frank felt the pressure, especially after Tom volunteered to coach Frank's baseball team in the Big Creek community of Acorn County in North Georgia – about forty miles north of Atlanta. Tom had never played baseball – not one day of his life had he played an organized baseball game. Yet Tom had some natural athletic ability. Tom was fast, had great hand-eye coordination, and was short, compact, and strong. He was determined that his oldest son – who shared none of his athleticism – was going to absorb athleticism that just wasn't in the boy's genes.

"Catch the damn ball," Tom said, losing every ounce of patience as he hit Frank ground balls in their home's front yard – balls that rolled through Frank's legs. "Son, put your glove on the ground and leave it there."

"Catch the damn ball," Tom shouted as he launched a fly ball in Frank's direction only to watch it drop near Frank's feet. "One of these balls is going to hit you in the head, and I guess you'll learn how to catch it then." That never happened because Tom made sure to hit the fly balls near Frank but not at him. He knew well that if he accidentally injured his oldest son, his wife, Janet, would kill him, and then his parents, R. C. and Kathryn Wilcox, would finish off whatever carcass Janet left for them.

"Hit the damn ball, Frank," Tom said, almost whining from exhausted frustration, throwing pitch after pitch for his son to hit. "How can you not hit the ball? If I throw it any slower, I'll be able to run up there and hit the damn thing myself."

That was just practice in the yard.

The pressure intensified when the Big Creek Dodgers gathered behind Big Creek Elementary School for their official practices during the season. It drove Tom crazy that baseball came so easy to some of the other boys while his son struggled so mightily. He took it personally. He blamed Janet's gene pool – though her only brother had been a good baseball player. Tom blamed the Lord. The more focused Tom became on Frank's shortcomings, the more Frank underperformed because of the stress.

Following one game, Tom received a call from an angry parent – not angry because of how Tom treated *her* son, but for how he publicly treated his own son – Frank. It was a first in all of Big Creek recreational baseball.

Frank's mama, Janet, finally intervened. She was not a wilting violet of a wife or woman and had no reservations when it came to identifying her husband's parenting mistakes.

"He thinks you hate him," she said one night after the boys – Frank, Jack, and Wayne – went to bed. "You have officially reached a new low, Tom Wilcox. People are noticing how hard you are on him – over a stupid baseball game."

"Well he doesn't like to hunt or fish either," Tom said. "He and I have nothing in common. We tried guitar lessons, but he gave up that too. All he wants to do is write those stories. Do you know he even asked me for a typewriter?"

Frank pulled his pillow over his head. He could hear every word of the conversation.

Through teary eyes, he had to smile.

He really did want a typewriter.

Frank's best-played game of those three springs came when his parents were out of town and the Dodgers played a Saturday game against the Acorn city team at the old town park. R. C. Wilcox piled his oldest grandson into his black Cadillac and drove him to the game to play. As Frank climbed out of the car, he noticed his grandfather was not coming with him.

"Are you coming, Papa?" he asked.

"No, it's too hot," his grandfather said. "I'll stay here and take a nap. You go have fun."

Frank had two singles in that game and played an error-free first base. The Dodgers lost, but Frank won the day. He even had the fans' support, and they cheered loudly for him.

Frank never forgot how much he enjoyed that single game – with not one member of his family watching him. For that one game, he felt like a baseball player.

Frank did love baseball.

He loved everything about it. Had anyone asked ten-year-old Frank Wilcox what he loved most, baseball would have ranked just below writing his short stories and below his mixed-breed dog, Duchess.

His love for baseball began in second grade. Frank's best friend, Charlie Keller, had invited him to a Friday night sleepover. After cheeseburgers, chips, and popcorn, the boys had settled in to watch television. That night featured the 1948 black-and-white movie *The Babe Ruth Story* featuring William Bendix in the title role as the legendary George Herman Ruth. Frank was captivated. He had to know more about this Babe Ruth.

Frank was already reading at an advanced level. The following Monday, he made his way to the Acorn Primary School's library, where he joined a long waiting list to read the Babe's simple biography in the Childhood of Famous Americans series. When Frank was finally able to read the biography, he read it four times in a single week. Because so many of his boyhood friends had read the Babe's story and were learning about baseball from their dads and other relatives, softball games popped up on the recess playground. The boys learned how to play this All-American game from one another.

Quiet, unassuming, and sensitive, Frank was almost always chosen last when teams were picked for the playground games, and he was always stuck out in the outfield with at least ten other boys assigned to chase down balls that got past the better athletes in the infield. Frank was usually the last batter to hit and almost always dribbled the ball weakly on the hard playground dirt or struck out altogether. If he reached base, it was because of an infield error. It was not unusual for a game to feature "last strikes," when a better hitter took over a weaker hitter's at-bat with two strikes. It was humiliating.

Despite it all, Frank loved baseball.

When his friends began collecting Topps baseball cards and playing for their community teams across Acorn County, Frank was swept away in all of it. He convinced Tom to sign him up, and Tom eagerly responded and even bought him a new Spalding glove at Holbrook's Hardware in downtown Acorn. That's when the backyard instruction began. A year later, when Frank's brother Jack, a much more gifted athlete, took up baseball, Frank became a partner with whom Jack could play in the yard. Those spring and summer sessions did little to improve Frank, but Jack became a better baseball player. To Frank's relief, Tom's focus shifted to Jack. Frank began writing fictional baseball stories.

To all this baseball hysteria among the boys of Acorn County came the Atlanta Braves.

In 1966, when Frank turned seven, the Braves, with their home run-hitting icon, Hank Aaron, relocated from Milwaukee to Atlanta. Babe Ruth might have long been buried, but Aaron was the next best thing, and he was now a Georgian. Frank learned from his friends that a simple transistor radio could pick up Braves games on Atlanta's WSB 750. R. C. Wilcox bought his grandson one of the small radios that came with an earphone, and Frank listened to the Braves every chance he got – even at night under the covers of the bed he shared with Jack.

Frank and Jack built healthy collections of the Topps baseball cards. Players on the same teams were bound with a rubber band, and Frank enjoyed collecting the starting lineups for each team. On

Friday nights, he and Jack used their cards to mimic actual games on the Wilcox family front room floor. When Atlanta's WSB television began airing the occasional Braves game on Friday nights, there was no bedtime.

When Frank reached the fourth grade, his beloved teacher, Mrs. Carolyn Hicks, arranged for him to read his short stories in her class and over the school's intercom system for the entire school. Many of them focused on sports, specifically baseball. Frank drew inspiration from the playground games, baseball books that he read, or games he watched on television.

About this time, the Atlanta Braves marketing department boosted its fan base by having designed community games at the stadium. During the summer after Frank's fourth-grade year, the Wilcox family joined hundreds of others for Acorn County's night at the big ballpark. The seats might have been in the upper deck, but they were right behind home plate. It was better than the circus or the Ice Capades in Atlanta. Now, the boys of Acorn watched their heroes live. During one of those games, Tom bought his oldest son a program, and Frank spent the entire game reading it, devouring stories about players, the Braves, and Major League Baseball.

What's more, there in the center of the program – where the staples bound pages together – Frank found two pages that forever changed his life. There he found pages for in-game score keeping. He had no idea how to use them, and there were no instructions, but he decided that he would learn how to fill in those pages during the course of the game.

The next week, he took the game's program to the Acorn County Library. The librarian, Mrs. Jean Potts, helped him find a book that included instructions on how to complete a player-by-player and inning-by-inning accounting of a baseball game. Frank borrowed the library book, and the very next Friday night, sitting in front of the family television, Frank labored over completing the blank scoring pages he had hand copied on ruled notebook paper.

The scoring pages helped him stay focused on the game, and he enjoyed reliving the game through the pages. He began to understand baseball strategy better, and though he still could not play well, he at least knew what was happening – often on a deeper level than those who excelled at the game.

Frank often visited Holbrook's Hardware on Acorn's downtown square. He loved visiting the hardware store, which was the only place in Acorn a boy could buy baseball equipment like gloves, baseballs, catcher's gear, and bats. Every piece of equipment the Wilcox boys owned came from this one store. When Frank was in town, he enjoyed visiting the store. It smelled like baseball – the leather, all the leather.

One afternoon, as he stood studying the wooden Louisville Slugger bat selection, something caught his eye. It was a spiral-bound book, and every page was a scoresheet. He opened it and fairly gasped in excitement. He purchased one of the books with a few dollars he had saved from working on his grandfather's hog farm. He then went to Jackson's 5 & 10 and purchased a box of Black Warrior No. 2 pencils. He was in heaven.

Janet Wilcox freaked out.

"You spent your money on this?" she said, waving the scorebook in the air. "This is a waste of money, Frank." She concluded that Frank's focus on baseball was becoming too much of an obsession, and for a short time, she took away his baseball cards and his new scorebook. She encouraged him to read more Scripture, which Frank didn't mind, but he harassed her daily to have his baseball back. Finally, she relented.

When Frank was eleven, Tom surprised the family with tickets to a Braves game against the expansion league Montreal Expos. Frank was especially excited because his first baseman's mitt – a surprise gift from Tom – was a Spalding with the stamped signature of the Expos first baseman, Ron Fairly. Frank used his own money to purchase a game program, borrowed one of two pencils he had given his mother for safe-keeping, and spent that game completing the scorebook. During the seventh inning, when his brothers went with Tom for ice cream, Frank stayed back because he did not want to miss one play, and was glad when Jack graciously returned with ice cream for him.

Frank did not realize it then, but his love for record keeping, statistics, and writing were going to come together in just a handful of years when, as a high school sophomore, he became the sportswriter for the *Acorn County News*. When he graduated high school, the school's Athletic Booster Club gave him a large trophy and a check for $200.

When his parents bought him a Strat-o-Matic baseball game for Christmas, he quickly ditched it and created his own game. While Strat-o-Matic used player cards, stat ratings, and dice to recreate baseball games, Frank's game included eight teams of imaginary players with random coin flips and intricate formulas to create games in a scorekeeper's book. Frank kept running statistics for each of his players, and those statistics affected the game's formulas, which allowed each game to be different based on the skills of the team's players. It all fueled more and more of the short stories he loved to write.

This boy struggled mightily to get a C in math – only because statistics and research were never a part of the curriculum.

Once Frank could drive, he forced his best friends – Pete Yancey and Wendell Mann – to attend every Braves home opener and sometimes games during the regular season. He often drove the forty miles south from Acorn to Atlanta to watch a game by himself. Sometimes he took his brothers or maybe a first cousin. While working at the *Acorn County News*, he wrote the Braves and requested press credentials that allowed him good seating behind home plate and a free hot dog.

Later, when he went to work for the *Atlanta Journal* and the *Atlanta Constitution* daily newspapers, he used Mondays at the main office on downtown Atlanta's Marietta Street to visit with the sports staff, including those who covered the Atlanta Braves daily. More than once, on a spring day, he drove over to an empty Atlanta Stadium, walked inside, and sat in the empty bleachers with his lunch – watching the grounds crew at work. It was there, one day, when he met his hero, Hank Aaron, who was walking in the concourse.

Frank played pickup baseball and softball through college with some moments of success as he physically filled out. Still, he was generally just a player needed to fill a position and not a player needed to win games. That was fine with him – he simply enjoyed being around the game, whether at Atlanta Stadium, watching it on television, playing Sunday afternoons on a dusty church field in Acorn County, or playing paper contests through his gaming system. It didn't matter to him. Frank Wilcox loved baseball, and he always kept a brand-new Rawlings baseball on his desk and sometimes rolled it around in his hand, feeling every one of its 108 red stitches.

⚾ ⚾ ⚾

On Easter Sunday that spring, the same early spring Frank had experienced melancholy on the porch swing, he and Vicki went through their morning ritual of getting dressed for church and hustling out the door. They were hosting an after-church luncheon for two of their adult sons and some friends, and both Frank and Vicki made sure the lunchtime fare was ready to pop into the oven as soon as they got home from church services.

"You know, every year at Easter, Jack and I got a new baseball and a new wooden baseball bat," Frank said. "It was our signal that baseball season had arrived. The baseball was a Wilson, and the bat was a Louisville Slugger. Mama alternated which of us received the bat and which one received the ball."

"I usually got a doll in my Easter basket," Vicki said, walking past him for the door. "Come on. We don't want to be late for church."

"I'm looking forward to watching the Braves on television this afternoon," Frank said. "I figure all this Easter excitement will be over, and everyone will be gone by three."

Vicki rolled her eyes at her six-foot curmudgeon. "Bah humbug. You have to snap out of this funk, Frank. It's starting to get on my nerves."

⚾ ⚾ ⚾

After lunch and a quick egg hunt among the adults, Frank settled into a recliner to watch the Braves that afternoon. The season had just started – this was the first week of the season. He invited his guests to watch the game with him, especially hoping his two sons

19

would stay, but they declined. They had places to go and people to see. Frank hugged them as they left, and then settled in to watch the Braves by himself.

In his lap was a scorebook. In his hand was a Black Warrior No. 2.

☻ ☻ ☻

The idea came to him that Easter night, lying on his back in the pitch dark of the bedroom. His mind raced around from the grave-yard in the backyard to the bat and ball of Easter baskets long ago, to the Braves game that afternoon, and to the scoring he had started in the scorebook before he fell asleep in the recliner.

Like his own Easter surprise, the idea just came to him, crashing through his springtime melancholy and providing light where there was darkness.

"Vicki," he said excitedly. He reached over and touched her back.

"What is it?" she asked, prepared to reject any frisky advances about to come her way.

"I'm going to a Braves game," Frank said.

She sighed. "Good. I'm trying to sleep."

"No, listen," Frank said.

"I don't want to listen," she said from her side of the dark of the bedroom, slung into the covers of their king-sized bed. She also had a pillow strategically placed in the center of the bed – sort of a wall to prevent Frank's restlessness from affecting her sleep. "I want to go to sleep. We have to work tomorrow."

"I'm going to look at the Braves schedule and find a weekday game in May. Then I'm going to buy the most expensive ticket I can afford – maybe one right behind home plate, lower level – and I'm going to that game all by my lonesome. I won't have to talk to anyone. I won't have to impress anyone. I can eat whatever I want. I can keep a scorebook. It will be fantastic."

"Okay, great," she said. "You do that. Goodnight."

Now that he was wide awake, excited once again, and knowing that she was awake, he thought he might as well try. "Vicki, permission to cross this wall for attempted lovemaking?"

"Permission denied," she said.

He stared at the ceiling and smiled. It was the first smile of the spring.

⚾ ⚾ ⚾

The next morning, before he went to work, Frank visited the Atlanta Braves website. He began searching weekday home games and ticket availability. He wanted to sit in the lower level of Turner Field, as close to home plate as he could get, and the cost of the ticket didn't matter.

"Crap," he said to himself as he clicked through game after game. The Braves had won eleven straight National League East pennants, and the fan frenzy had not abated one bit in recent years. Tickets were always a little scarce at the start of the season as excited fans shook off the winter slump and got back out to the ballpark.

Frank found a Wednesday in mid-May with a $50 ticket on row 16 right behind home plate on the same level with the dugouts. The Braves were playing the Florida Marlins, who that year were going to finish one game behind the Braves in the standings. This early season contest between two competitive teams promised to be exciting and competitive.

Before he purchased the ticket, Frank paused and considered asking Vicki if she wanted to go, but then thought differently of it. *He wanted to go by himself.* With his credit card information punched into the online system, he clicked the Purchase button, and his plan was launched.

🔵 🔵 🔵

When that May Wednesday – the Wednesday after Mother's Day – arrived, Frank could hardly contain himself. He had told no one but Vicki about his plans for that evening.

He wasn't concerned about the drive from Concord, South Carolina, to Atlanta's Turner Field – it was only two hundred miles due west, and he could easily make the drive in three hours. To ensure unexpected traffic delays didn't hamper his progress, he planned to leave Concord early in the afternoon, even if he had to sit in the car and wait on everything at the ballpark to come to life.

🔵 🔵 🔵

Turner Field had opened as the home ballpark to the Atlanta Braves for the 1997 season. The stadium was originally built as the centerpiece for the 1996 Summer Olympic Games and was named Centennial Olympic Stadium. When the Olympics ended that summer, work began almost immediately to refit the stadium as the Braves' new home. Turner Field was named after Georgia's Ted

Turner, who was an international communication mogul and had purchased the Braves in the nation's bicentennial year – 1976 – and used the purchase to reverse the fortunes of his failing television station, WTCG. Airing all of the Braves games on the television station expanded the Braves to the "team of the South" and launched the WTBS national superstation.

The Braves were never considered an every-year playoff team. They won the Western Division in 1969 but then lost to the Miracle Mets in the National League title series. In 1982, they lost another National League title series, this time against the St. Louis Cardinals. The 1991 season changed everything; it was the "worst to first year." In 1990, the Braves twenty-fifth season in Atlanta, the team finished last in the Western Division with a record of 65-97. In the offseason, the Braves added key veterans to complement a young, talented roster. In 1991, the Braves won the Western Division with a record of 94-68, besting the Los Angeles Dodgers, which finished one game behind them at 93-69.

Further, the Braves defeated the Pirates in the National League Championship Series, facing the Minnesota Twins (another worst-to-first team that year) in the World Series. The Braves and Twins, similar in many ways, fought to the World Series's seventh game before the Twins won the game and the championship, 1-0 in ten innings. Three of the seven World Series games that year went to extra innings.

Despite losing the World Series, baseball euphoria erupted in Atlanta over the Braves' success. The Braves did not disappoint in 1992 or several years afterward, winning their division title and playing in the Major League Baseball playoffs. The team won the World Series in 1995 against the Cleveland Indians.

⚾ ⚾ ⚾

Frank had driven to the old Atlanta Stadium almost as soon as he had gotten his Georgia driver's license. He had shuttled his brothers – Jack and Wayne – to games and had driven his friends there, and several high school and college dates included a Braves game. From Acorn, he was completely comfortable driving to the stadium, getting through Atlanta's downtown connector – the merger of Interstates 75 and 85 – up and around the State Capitol on Capitol Avenue and then to the stadium's Orange Lot. It was easy-peasy.

Now, living in the Midlands of South Carolina, the drive was longer but just as easy. Living two miles from Interstate 20, he could jump on the westbound freeway and drive nonstop to the Hill Street exit in downtown Atlanta. From the top of the Hill Street exit ramp, it was left back over the interstate bridge, and a right at the light, and then a few blocks to the stadium's Orange Lot on the left. It was also easy-peasy.

"Are you sure you want to do this by yourself?" Vicki asked him. "Don't you want to ask one of the boys? What about Doc?"

"Hell no," Frank said. "I want to go so I can just focus on the game with no distractions. I want to soak up the baseball. I want to keep my book."

She raised an eyebrow.

"You aren't a distraction," he said, "but this will be fun for me and a little therapeutic."

She smiled and waved him off. "Say hello to your girlfriend."

"No one but you could live with an eccentric, moody old bastard like me," he said.

"True," she said. "I am the only one for you."

⚾ ⚾ ⚾

The drive to Turner Field was without issue that day. He left Concord at 1:00 p.m., knowing he could beat Atlanta's rush-hour traffic coming in the opposite direction to the suburbs of Conyers and Covington. The stadium opened at 4:35 p.m. – three hours before the game began at 7:35. Frank was reading – or rather rereading for perhaps the fifth time – Roger Kahn's 1972 nonfiction classic titled *The Boys of Summer* about the Brooklyn Dodgers and their victory in the 1955 World Series. When he arrived at the stadium's Orange Lot, he parked his car in the largely empty parking lot, lay across the front bench seat of his F-150, and began reading his book. He planned to stay here until the stadium opened then make his way inside for batting practice and a Georgia dog – a delicious, giant hot dog heaped with mustard, Vidalia onion relish, and coleslaw.

He fell asleep in his truck as the May afternoon sunshine warmed the truck and lulled him to sleep. Fortunately, he was startled awake by slamming doors around him as the parking lot began to fill up. Slightly disoriented, he turned his neck to the right and left and pulled his feet around so he was sitting on the passenger's side. His book had fallen into the floorboard, awkwardly landing and bending some of the pages.

He rubbed his eyes and smiled at some of those walking by and staring in. It was odd to see a grown man, by himself, in the passenger's side of a gray Ford pickup here in the Orange Lot of Turner Field. Stepping out of the truck, Frank was glad he had brought a jacket. It was cool for mid-May, with the temperature a pleasant 65 and expected to drop down to 55 by the end of the game.

Frank pulled on the jacket and started toward the stadium, carrying, in one hand, a brown, spiral-bound *C. S. Peterson's Scoremaster Scorebook*. It was just like the ones he had used every season he had coached the Sharks of the Concord Dixie Baseball League. The new scorebook was a virgin one – bought for this occasion and with all the pages clean. Frank reached to his head and felt the two freshly sharpened Black Warrior pencils stuck in under his hat just in front of his ears, where his glasses helped hold them in place. He stopped and double-checked to ensure he had his ticket, wallet, and telephone. He clicked the lock button on his truck fob once more for good measure.

"Here we go," he thought, and smiled, walking toward Capitol Avenue and the big brick stadium that was the home of his Atlanta Braves. "This is going to be awesome."

Getting inside the stadium early, Frank didn't have to wait long for a Georgia dog. Combined with an "ice-cold beer – right here!" it was the perfect ballpark supper. In fact, out of excitement more than hunger, he bought two Georgia dogs, found a picnic table near the outfield seats, and sat down to eat his supper – or at least the first round of his supper. He planned to eat his way out of this stadium over the next few hours.

After the foot-long hot dogs, Frank sat in right-center field and watched batting practice. Then he walked one and a half laps around the lower level concourse and found his aisle at Section 102. An usher checked his ticket to ensure he wasn't an interloper from the upper decks. Approved for entry, Frank made his way down the long concrete steps to row 16 and then slid into seat number 3.

To his right sat a long row of men that he quickly identified as being from out of town but in Atlanta on business. They had decided to take in a game but were more interested in talking and drinking beer than watching the game. To Frank's left, seats number 1 and 2 were soon filled by a young couple that Frank estimated were in their thirties. The young man wore a No. 10 Chipper Jones baseball jersey. Frank tried hard not to notice what the young woman was wearing, or rather what she wasn't. Her generously enhanced breasts strained against the cotton fabric of a tank top. The strain was so much that the word "Braves" across her chest was stretched into three syllables.

It was going to be a long game, especially with the row of businessmen straining to look left like a gaggle of goofy adolescent boys fighting over their first *Playboy* magazine. Frank had to tune all of this out. He was settling in to concentrate on the field preparations when he took a kick to the head, turned around, and got an "I'm so sorry" from the wife of a couple probably ten years older than him.

"No problem at all," he said. "At least you didn't spill beer on me, which almost always happens."

The businessman next to him, introduced as Phil, said, "It's a long game, brother." He laughed while holding up his beer in a mock toast. Frank just smiled, thinking, "Please don't make me beat you before these three hours are over."

Squeezing into the row in front of him, Frank supposed, was a dad, a grandad, and the dad's two young sons. The dad smiled at Frank as he sat down, and then awkwardly paused when he spotted the young woman sitting beside Frank. The man tried not to stare a second time as he sat down, and Frank wanted to laugh out loud.

The rest of the seats were filling in all around them, and for a Wednesday in the spring, Frank thought the lower bowl was pretty full, especially here by home plate. He had rarely ever been able to spring for a $50 seat down here, so he didn't know what to expect about the crowd.

Deciding he had better use the bathroom before the game started, he excused himself past the young couple and stepped onto the concrete steps. He returned with another beer and squeezed past the couple. Before he sat down, he reached his hand out to the young man and said, "As long as we are sitting here together, I might as well introduce myself. My name is Frank." The young man smiled and introduced himself simply as "Bradley." Frank thought it best not to be forward and sat down when Bradley didn't introduce the young woman. He put the beer in a cup holder and opened the scorebook.

Apologetically, the young woman immediately said, "My name is Whitney." Frank smiled at her.

On the other side of Frank, Phil gave half a wave in her direction and said, "Phil here. Nice to meet you." She ignored him.

The Braves' and Marlins' lineups were being announced on the large outfield screen, and Frank pulled a Black Warrior pencil from under the band of his cap and marked down the lineups.

"Oh, you are a scorekeeper," Phil said. "I never could focus on a full baseball game and record all those plays."

"It does take concentration," Frank said. "This is a luxury for me. Normally, I've had my family with me, and it's tough to pay close attention with small children around." He smiled before saying, "And talking all the time." Phil got the message, lifting his beer in another toast.

The dad in front turned his head and said, "Tell me about it." He laughed and nodded his head to his right and the two excited but well-behaved young boys. "I'm not sure that I'll see much of this game."

"You won't regret bringing those boys to a game," Frank said. "And one day, they will be gone, and you will find yourself here by yourself."

The grandad said, "I keep telling him that boys grow up and then old Daddy just becomes dumb Daddy. Right, now he's still a hero, and he better enjoy that."

"Dad," the man said, smiling, "I don't think you're dumb. Goofy, maybe, but not dumb."

At Frank's right, Phil asked about Frank's family, and Frank gave him a brief answer. Frank did not want to have a game-long conversation with Phil. The purpose of coming alone was to be alone and focus on the game. He did smile when he thought how ridiculous that proposition might be now that he was here. Had he wanted to be alone, he should have sat in the far reaches of the upper deck – probably where he belonged. Baseball was a pretty slow, boring grind of a game, and being in the stands easily became a social event with the game happening in the background. Still, he thought, "If I just focus on this scorebook, maybe they will leave me alone."

The national anthem was sung by a trio from an Atlanta-area high school chorus, and Frank stood with all the others in the stadium. He stood at attention with his right hand formally across his heart as he had been taught in Acorn's Boy Scout Troop 39, long ago.

He smiled at the little boys in front of him. They had removed their Braves baseball caps and had hands over their hearts even as they twirled because of the excitement of the game.

Frank thought it was unusually funny that when Braves fans sang the national anthem, there was always extra emphasis on the final verse, "O say, does that star-spangled banner yet wave, O'er the land of the free and the home of the BRAVE?" Many of the questionable patriotic always shouted "BRAVES" instead of "brave" at the end of the anthem, turning the lyrics from lawyer Francis Scott Key's 1814 poem into a Major League Baseball fight song.

As Frank and his new community of friends sat down, Frank smiled and breathed in the atmosphere around him.

FIRST INNING
DANIEL

Extra, extra, read all about it!
Daniel got a single, and I'm gonna shout it!
Daniel got a single!

Following the national anthem, there were a few other announcements, and then Alfredo Amezaga, the Marlins' left fielder, walked to the plate to lead off the game. As he did, Frank's attention was diverted to a few rows down to his left. A large man was ushering two small boys ahead of him into a row. One of the boys was tiny with a Braves cap pulled too far down on his head. The other boy was excitedly jumping around and acting goofy – like all excited little boys are prone to do. Watching the older boy, the smaller boy just stared at him, grinning from ear to ear and saying nothing.

At one point, the smiling little boy turned and, certainly unintentionally, made eye contact with Frank. Frank smiled and thought of Daniel.

Frank Wilcox was a twenty-two-year-old newspaper reporter in Southeast Georgia. About an hour's drive southwest of Savannah, the city of Jenson was sequestered from big-city influences. Yet its economy was thriving because of a large paper mill that attracted small businesses and state government satellite offices. Everyone knew everyone in Jenson, and generational family ties ran deep. Frank Wilcox, a North Georgia boy, was an immediate stranger – a new kid in school – but Jenson's loving people met newcomers with open arms.

Jenson's population was just under ten thousand. Cherry Street cut through the center of town, posing as the main street. Just past two blocks of thriving downtown businesses and across the railroad tracks, Cherry Street's business district gave way to a beautiful, tree-lined residential area with the First Baptist Church and the First United Methodist Church on opposite corners as brick-and-mortar sentinels for the residential community. For the most part, through healthy small businesses and a great chamber of commerce, Jenson had just about everything its citizenry needed. For getaways, Savannah was just over an hour away to the northeast, and the white-sand Georgia beaches were an hour due south. Jenson was a small-town dream community.

After graduating from the University of Georgia, he had returned to his hometown of Acorn, working for the *Acorn County News*, where he had worked through high school and breaks during college. In the year between graduation and moving to Jenson, he met the love of his life, Vicki Hill, and they started dating seriously. He had no immediate plans to leave Acorn, where his parents and all of his high school friends lived just north of Atlanta.

As fate often calls, the telephone rang one Friday morning at his office. It was the owner of the *Jenson County Press*, calling to discuss a news and sports writing job. Frank knew Georgia newspapers. He had attended college on a grant from the Georgia Press Association, which opened his eyes and ears to the good and bad Georgia newspapers. The *Jenson County Press* was at the top of the good category – so good that Frank had written a college paper about the newspaper's award-winning layout and design.

The newspaper's owner offered Frank a job, and Frank took it, knowing the transition so far from home would be hard. He was leaving Vicki, but to be honest, she was about to start college, and her parents had already moved to Texas. He and Vicki were facing a long-distance relationship regardless of where Frank lived. He was also leaving his hometown's security for a place three hundred miles from home and where he knew no one except the newspaper owner. It was hard to imagine a more jolting transition to the system, outside of joining the United States military.

Tom Wilcox helped his oldest son move to Jenson. Frank rented a one-bedroom apartment, two blocks off Cherry Street. Sara Watson, an elderly widow, had renovated her ranch-style home to create an apartment on the northern end. A sliding door with a latch on either side separated the apartment from her larger side of the home. In that apartment, Frank had a large bedroom that was also his living space. The only other room was a bathroom; a tiny kitchen had been built inside a hallway. Mrs. Watson controlled the thermostat from her side of the house, but she liked her house cool in the hot south Georgia summers, which was fine with Frank. On more than one occasion, she tapped on Frank's door in the evenings and invited him to join her for supper. Over time, as trust built, she permitted him to watch the color television on her side of the house when she was out of town. She had cable television; Frank did not. So her television opened up the ability to watch the Atlanta Braves on Ted Turner's TBS superstation.

Frank joined the First Baptist Church and attended a singles Sunday school class. He also got involved in charitable causes, joined the annual community talent and comedy revue cast, and started feeling like a Jenson resident in just a year. He loved the people, and they loved him. In a very short time, Jenson felt like home.

Winters in the Deep South did not last long. In South Georgia, the winters were just a colder version of the fall, which was summer without daylight savings time or the blanketing humidity. Because of the climate, outdoor recreation occasionally paused but never really stopped, and conversations about spring sports for adults and children began in January rather than in late March, April, and May.

Frank's desk at the *Jenson County Press* was in the center of a large room shared by two other writers and two women who sold advertisements for the twice-weekly newspaper. There was a constant hum of activity, and Frank often found the loud conversations a distraction to his best writing. He regularly returned to the office in the evenings and wrote his stories in the empty newspaper office's quiet. Because he didn't have a typewriter at home, evenings at the newspaper office also gave him opportunity to write the occasional short story.

One evening, in late winter, he was sitting at his desk, pounding out a story from the week's meeting of the Jenson Town Council, when he was startled by the loud ringing of the telephone on his desk. He let out a long sigh and growled and then picked up the telephone.

"*Jenson County Press*," he said into the receiver, his voice transmitting a little too much of his aggravation at being disturbed.

"Hey, Frank," a familiar voice greeted him. "This is Terry over at the recreation department. I drove by your office and saw your car out front. Can I come over and visit with you for just a few minutes?"

Frank liked Terry Thompson a lot. Now in his thirties, Terry had been a local baseball player who went on to be a college baseball player – even playing on the roster of the University of Georgia. He then coached at Jenson County High School. Now he was the director of the local recreation department through which all Jenson youth sports were funneled under the statewide umbrella of the Georgia Recreation and Parks Society – the GRPS.

"Sure," Frank said. "I'll meet you at the front door and unlock it."

Frank finished the paragraph he was writing. He walked across the large room, his dress shoes click-clacking on the linoleum tile floor, and pushed open a swinging door that led to the newspaper office's lobby. He walked around the front counter and smiled at Terry, who was waiting on him to open the door.

Terry shook his hand and said, "Working hard or hardly working?"

"Sometimes it's easier to concentrate here in the evenings, by myself," Frank said. "I don't do well with a lot of distraction when I'm trying to concentrate. I get irritated."

The newspaper office's large lobby had several comfortable vinyl chairs – a waiting room far too large for the traffic that came to the newspaper office. The large room did provide a lot of wall space for the many awards won by the newspaper.

"I have a problem," Terry said. "I think you can be a solution."

Frank led Terry to the vinyl chairs, and the two men sat at a ninety-degree angle to one another. Frank put his feet up on a coffee table. "I'll do whatever I can to help. Have we done something wrong? I can't think of anything we've written that would have caused you a problem . . ."

Terry shook his head. "No, I'm not here to complain. I'm not even here about the newspaper. I'm here to see you."

"Okay," Frank said, smiling nervously with furrowed eyebrows.

"I need a baseball coach for one of our younger teams this spring," Terry said. "I've got a team with no coach, and I just thought you might be able to do it for us."

Frank stared at him and began backpedaling. "I don't know."

"You know baseball," Terry said. "You write sports. You are also single, so you have some time. I think you would be great at coaching in our league."

Frank laughed and tossed his head back against the chair's padding, resting it there and staring at the ceiling. "I've never done anything like this," he said. "How old are they?"

"They are nine- and ten-year-old boys," Terry said. "Depending on the birthdays, there might be one or two eight-year-olds, but they will be nine this summer."

Frank stared at him, thinking hard about this unexpected request.

"We provide you with all the equipment you'll need, and all the games are right here at the Morris recreation complex just outside the city," he said. "We'll even schedule practice times for you at the fields. You show up and coach."

"There might be weekends when I can't be here," Frank said, knowing he would want to see Vicki on spring weekends before she left for the summer in Texas.

"Listen, we'll make sure you have one or two dads to help you, and they can sub for you when you are out of town."

Frank sat in silence and then said, "Why not just ask the dads to do it?"

"Many of them work at the paper mill, and their schedules can be unpredictable," Terry said, "That's why I need you. I've got a team of little boys who want to play baseball, but no one is able or willing to help them." He shrugged his shoulders.

Frank looked at him and then looked away.

Terry could see he wasn't going to get an answer, and he didn't want Frank to say no too quickly. He stood up. "Think about it. Let me know in a day or two, okay? I don't want to talk you into it. I want you to do it because you want to serve."

"Alright," Frank said. He walked Terry to the front door, shook his hand as he walked out the door, and then locked the door behind him.

Frank sat down at his desk and tried to work, but he couldn't. He finally went home, continuing to think of the reasons he was too busy and too inexperienced to coach a baseball team.

The next afternoon, he walked into the newspaper office, pushed past the big swinging door, and walked to his desk. Taped to the receiver of his telephone was a small pink paper inviting him to return the telephone call of Terry Thompson at the recreation department.

Frank wadded up the paper and threw it in the trashcan. He wasn't finished thinking about it. Didn't Terry Thompson know he had been a terrible baseball player? Didn't Terry Thompson know he had only played baseball for three years? Didn't Terry Thompson know that Frank was almost always the last one picked when teams were chosen?

⚾ ⚾ ⚾

Frank was too poor to have a telephone in Mrs. Watson's apartment. Many nights, after prearranging schedules, he walked to the Zippy Mart, two-tenths of a mile away on Cherry Street, and used a pay telephone to call Vicki in Athens.

"I've been asked to coach a baseball team," he said as an old dog sat in the middle of the store's parking lot, staring at him.

"A baseball team?" Vicki asked, and he was not amused that she was so surprised. "Is that something you can do?"

"Yes, *I can do it*," he said indignantly. "What about the few weekends you have left in school? I want to see you – not be here coaching baseball on Saturday mornings."

"In June, I'll go see Mama and Daddy in Texas for the summer," she said. "You might like having something to do."

"But what about weekends between now and then?" he said, half hoping she would rescue him from this dilemma.

"I like baseball," she said. "Daddy was the commissioner of the league when I was little. I'll come down there on some weekends and watch your team."

"So you think I should do it?" Frank asked once more.

"I think you are going to do exactly what you want to do, Frank Wilcox," she said. "If you want to do it, don't worry about me. Do it."

He paused, watching the dog get up and walk across the parking lot toward Cherry Street.

She made it too easy. After more chit-chat, he told her that he loved her and then hung up the telephone's receiver. As he walked back to Mrs. Watson's house, in the shadowed sidewalks of Plum Street, Frank knew Terry would need an answer the next day.

"I don't even think I have my glove down here," he said to himself.

⚾ ⚾ ⚾

Frank did have his glove. When he got home that night, he opened his closet and rummaged through a box. It was in there – a well-oiled, brown leather Spalding fielders glove he had bought while in college.

He decided to flip a quarter nine times, "Heads I do it, and tails I don't," and let fate decide what he should do. The answer gave him no peace.

He half-heartedly tossed up a prayer. "Lord, do you think I can do this?"

Be a servant.

The next morning, on the way to the newspaper office, he stopped at the recreation department's office. Terry Thompson was standing outside, casually talking to an outdoor crew about to begin their day. He smiled when he saw Frank.

"Well?" he said. "Are you a baseball coach?"

"Do you have a list of the players?" Frank asked.

"Well, Frank, there's a draft next Monday," Terry said. "You will have some players coming back from last year, but you'll have to draft players to fill the roster."

"I don't know any of the players," Frank said. "How can I draft a team?"

"I'll help you," Terry said. "And you get the first pick in the draft." He grimaced. Frank had an idea of what he was about to say next. "Yes, this was the worst team in the league last year; that's why you get the first pick this year."

"I don't know," Frank said. "I've got a million reasons to say no to this."

Terry shrugged. "Again, I can't talk you into it. You have to want to do it. Let me know before the day is out." He walked into the office. "If you are worried that you aren't qualified, let me just say this one thing. Yes, you can."

Frank got in his car and drove two blocks down South Brunswick Street to the intersection with Cherry Street. A red light at the intersection stopped him. At his right was his church, the First Baptist Church.

"When you get to a new place," his Mema, Carolyn Holmes, advised him, "visit the local chamber of commerce because they know everything about the community, and then find a church home. You won't find perfect people at the church, but you will find people struggling to do the right thing, and they will take care of you. You can serve alongside them."

He smiled at the big brick church building.

"And, Frank," she said, "I don't know how long you will be there, but bloom where you are planted. Get involved in your home."

Right then, her words seemed to come blistering out of that church building. When the light turned green, Frank turned right on Cherry, made his way around the block, and returned to the recreation department. No matter what he was or wasn't when he walked through those glass doors, when he came back out, Frank Wilcox was a baseball coach.

⚾ ⚾ ⚾

The draft went as well as could have been expected. The other seven coaches in the room grumbled that Terry was helping Frank, and further grumbled that Frank was getting the first pick of the draft. Some argued that a random draw should set the draft order. More than once, Terry reminded them that the draft rules were set and would not be changed. Everyone conceded that the first pick was a nine-year-old named Billy, who could do it all – hit, pitch, and field. Terry was quick to point out that Billy's dad would help Frank coach the team. That brought another round of lamentations.

"Any time you can draft a great player with a dad who can help you, it's a sweet deal," Terry said in a whisper. "You will need to remember that in future years." Frank laughed.

"Future years," Frank said back to him with a scoff at the prophetic attempt.

The draft lasted almost two hours, and Terry helped Frank though there were whispers with every pick that the department director's involvement wasn't fair.

"No one helped me in my first year," one man said. He wore a T-shirt with the word "Win" across the front of it. He was also missing a front tooth, which Frank thought might be a priority over winning.

"Mike, you grew up here," Terry said, laughing. "Besides, no one wants to help you. You are a jerk." Everyone laughed, including Mike, who just shrugged his shoulders. It was all good-natured; no one was really upset that Terry was helping Frank. They were each sure they were going to beat Frank's team.

When the draft concluded and the coaches left the office, Terry made a prediction for Frank's team. "You will do better than this team did last year – just on talent. You're strong at catcher and the corners, and you've got two pitchers who can alternate between pitching and shortstop. One of them, Faris, will be an All-Star for sure."

Terry advised Frank to call his players about the first practice but assured him the recreation department would notify all players of their team assignment and provide them with the league's practice schedule for their team.

⚾ ⚾ ⚾

On the day of the first practice, Frank was nervous all day. Word had leaked out around the newspaper office that he was coaching baseball, and colleagues questioned why he wanted to tie up so much time when he already worked so much at the newspaper. He had no answer for them.

He arrived at the recreation complex fields early, making sure he was the first one at practice. He stood outside the first base dugout, tossing a brand-new baseball in the air and catching it. Terry had personally delivered the team's equipment to the newspaper office, and the equipment left a lot to be desired. Aside from a canvas bag of baseballs – about half of which were new – there was an old army surplus bag of old, worn catcher's equipment and some old batting helmets. Someone had written "1964 Champs" in one helmet, dating it to twenty years before. Another helmet was labeled on the inside, "Big Mama's Country Cooking," as a nod to a previous team's sponsor.

Frank had also been given the team's uniforms – green hats with a scripted R on them for ITT Rayonier, the team's sponsor. ITT Rayonier, the community's large paper mill, was Jenson's largest employer and a significant economic contributor, resting alongside the Altamaha River. The green jerseys had the words "ITT Rayonier" in gold across the front. Frank immediately thought of the Oakland Athletics and wondered if any of his players would make the connection to a West Coast, American League team.

The team began arriving, boys accompanied by their parents – including several of the dads. Terry had helped him work out a simple plan for practice, and Frank invited the boys to come on the field, take a baseball, and begin playing catch with a friend. He introduced himself to each of the players. As the players warmed up, Frank could feel the suspicion in some of the parents – this was a boy coaching their boys, and this boy wasn't going to be as dedicated as one of the grown men they knew from church or the Moose Lodge.

Faris was the best player on the team, and everyone knew it. He was an athletic boy who could play anywhere and do anything. He also had a great attitude, representing a family that taught their children well. A boy named Joel announced himself as the catcher, and Frank sized him up as a natural-born leader. He was talkative, but not too much so; he encouraged the other boys vocally and he worked hard. David had played some first before. Mark took third. A short, athletic spitfire of a boy named Chris walked to second base as if he owned it and dared anyone to challenge for it. Billy and Faris went to the shortstop position. A long, lean boy named Jeff trotted to center field as if he was born to play it. He had speed and could cover a lot of ground. The rest of the team scattered in the outfield.

"Where's Daniel?" Frank asked, noting that every other player was at practice.

"He's not coming," Robert said, almost apologetically. "He can't always get a ride here."

⚾ ⚾ ⚾

The recreation department allowed almost a month of practices, twice each week, before the season's opening day, and Frank planned to take advantage of every time he was assigned a field for practice. With some dads' help, many of whom had grown up playing in this same league, Frank organized a practice routine that involved warming up, taking infield and outfield, and then working through batting practice, so each player got several swings on the ball. Whatever time was left at the end of practice, Frank let the boys choose teams and play a scrimmage among themselves. He and the dads often participated in the scrimmages, helping in the outfield and batting from the plate's opposite side. Frank usually threw batting practice because he could throw strikes and encourage players as they hit.

Frank had nowhere to be after practice, so he sometimes allowed them to go until dark, raising the temper of the moms. When the boys got home, they had supper to eat and homework to do, and bedtimes were starting to get later and later.

Frank was oblivious until Billy's dad pulled him aside at the start of one practice.

"The mamas are starting to complain some," the big, kind man said. "We are going to need to have them home by suppertime. It's probably a good idea to end practice before the boys want it to end. That way they will look forward to coming to the next one. If you practice too long and hard, it becomes like work, and you won't get their best."

Frank started to protest but didn't. The advice was sound. He allowed that quiet guidance to guide him the rest of his coaching days, and Frank became a master of the well-organized ninety-minute practice.

After ten days of practice, the twelve-man roster had slimmed to eleven because the boy named Daniel had still not been to practice. Frank decided to call Terry Thompson about what to do.

"I've called, and there's been no answer at his house," Frank said.

"Have you been by his house?" Terry asked. Frank said he had not, and that led Terry to hand out the boy's address. "I think we should make every effort to help this little boy get involved. His house isn't very far from the newspaper office. I'm not telling you to do it, but you might offer to help with transportation if his family needs it."

Frank trusted Terry's counsel, but he also knew deep down that an eleven-man roster was more favorable than a twelve-man roster, especially in terms of competitiveness. He had no assurance from any of the other players that Daniel would help the team win games. Still, he needed to do the right thing, which meant going to Daniel's house to check on him.

🔵🔵🔵

Daniel lived on Parkston Street, which was only three blocks from the newspaper office. Frank had now lived in Jenson County for a full year and had never been to this part of town – he had no reason to go there. Parkston Street was a narrow street with small brick ranch-style homes built, lining both sides of the street. There were big pine trees in the yard, which were covered with a carpet of pine needles. The houses had screen doors that kept the bugs out but provided poor ventilation for homes with no central air-conditioning. Nice-sized front porches were places to rest and listen to the murmur of the nearby Georgia Southern Railway's evening freight cars.

Frank looked at a piece of paper with Daniel's address scribbled on it. None of the houses were marked, so he used his best intuition to determine which it might be. Frank had delivered newspapers in college and knew that even-numbered houses were usually on the street's right side when turning off major thoroughfares. He turned his Chevy into a single-car driveway and got out of the car. As he walked toward the porch, an older woman stepped outside to meet him.

"Yes, sir?" she asked him.

"Ma'am, I'm looking for a boy named Daniel. He was signed up to play baseball, and I'm his coach this year," Frank said. "We've been practicing for two weeks and . . ."

She turned toward the screen door and shouted, "Daniel! Please come here!"

The seconds turned to slow-motion minutes as Frank stood there looking around while the woman on the porch smiled and sized him up. Finally, the screen door pushed open and the smallest nine-year-old boy Frank had ever seen stepped onto the porch. The boy looked down at his feet.

"This is Daniel," the woman said kindly as an introduction.

"Hello, Daniel," Frank said. "I'm your baseball coach this year, and I just came to see if you still want to play and how I can help you get to practices."

"My husband uses our car for work, and we don't have another one," the woman said. "I want him to play, but, Coach, we don't have a car that I can use. I was hoping he would be on the same team with one of our neighbors." She looked up and down the street.

Frank stared at the little boy. He knew he had to help.

"I work at the newspaper," Frank said, pointing back toward town in the general direction of the office. "Daniel, you be ready for me tomorrow at about five, and I'll come by and get you." He turned to the woman. "I'll bring him home right after practice, probably about seven."

"He'll be ready, sir," she said, and turned back into the house. Daniel stared at Frank, then followed her inside and never said a word.

⚾ ⚾ ⚾

After work the next day, Frank drove to the Parkston Street house and parked along the street. He got out of the car and waited beside it. Frank heard the woman shout, "Daniel!" and the little boy walked out of the house, wearing what Frank supposed he wore to school that day. He did have a baseball glove, and he wore a baseball cap with a tractor company's patch on the front.

Frank walked around to his Chevy's trunk, opened it, and pulled out one of the green team hats. He shut the trunk door and saw Daniel standing beside the car. He walked over and handed him the cap.

"Put this one on instead," Frank smiled. "You will officially be part of the team." Daniel looked at the ground and shyly smiled.

They got in the Chevy, and Frank drove to the recreation complex and the team's practice. As they rode, Frank did his best to talk to Daniel, but the little boy just stared out the passenger window, his head barely able to see out of the window, and he didn't say anything.

At practice, Frank and Daniel walked up with other team members who were gathering for practice. Robert knew Daniel right away and walked up to him. Robert said something, and Daniel nodded and smiled. When Frank officially introduced Daniel to the team, the boys were gracious, or they didn't say anything at all; Joel, the catcher, loudly welcomed the little boy to the team.

"Coach," Joel said a few minutes later as Frank stood beside his catcher to begin defensive practice, "Daniel is so little he will walk every time he comes up to bat. If he's fast, he can score every time."

"Well, we want him to hit, but, yes, he's small, alright," Frank said without looking at his catcher.

Daniel struggled to catch the ball from lack of any experience, so Frank paired him with Robert because the two boys knew one another and would both play in the outfield. Frank knew Robert would be patient and kind with him, and Robert could quietly help Daniel improve.

On the drive back to Parkston Street, Frank and Daniel rode in silence. Frank decided just to leave the little boy alone. He would talk when he was good and ready.

⚾⚾⚾

Frank walked in Terry Thompson's office, waving a piece of paper. He wasn't happy.

"You are throwing me to the wolves here," Frank said. "We get two preseason scrimmages, and my first one is against Burger King? They will kill us, which will be demoralizing to a team that finished in last place last year. Come on, Terry."

Terry laughed. "Congratulations, Coach."

Frank looked at him, puzzled.

"Yes sir, Frank, you are officially a coach in the Jenson baseball league," Terry said. "Whining and complaining are what gave it away." He laughed to himself while staring at Frank. "You'll be fine. We don't even turn on the scoreboard. The scrimmage is a chance to test boys at different positions, let them see some live pitching, and get your team legs under you before the first game. Have fun. Don't worry about winning or losing."

Burger King had not won the championship the year before, but they were now loaded for a title run. They had four All-Stars returning and a trio of ten-year-old pitchers who looked like giants on the pitcher's mound.

Hopes were high when the boys wearing ITT Rayonier-green stepped on the field against Burger King that Tuesday night. True enough, scoreboards were not on for preseason scrimmages, but every single person attending – including all the players – were keeping score. Mark, the third baseman, even marked both teams' runs in the dugout floor's dust.

Frank's pitching strategy was simple. He was going to rotate Faris and Billy from shortstop to the mound, starting with the younger Billy and using Faris, the All-Star, as a closer. If either of them were sick or got in trouble, Frank would bring in Jeff from center because the lanky kid was intimidating on the mound and could throw hard, if not always accurately.

The scrimmage was a massacre.

By the end of two innings, Burger King led 10-1 and never looked back. Billy's control was excellent, but the older boys pounded the ball to the outfield, and players ran the bases like they were on a merry-go-round. Faris had doubled and scored on a base hit by David, the first baseman. Burger King finished off the game in the last four innings, intentionally slowing down some, but still winning 15-1.

Frank was humiliated. He could almost hear those playground boys back in Acorn, laughing at him. He was no good as a player, and he was no better as a coach. Frank had better just stick to keeping score in a scorebook and writing his stories.

Frank leaned back against the dugout fence and tried to make light of it in the dugout with his stunned team. "Boys, that was a whopper of a loss." A few of the parents chuckled, but overall the joke fell flat. "Listen, we'll just come back out here on Thursday and practice and keep working on getting better. We already know they are the best team in the league. Not every team we face will be that good, and we'll win some, I promise. Let's not get discouraged, and keep working."

He had bought twelve packs of plain M&Ms and handed them out as the boys left the dugout. One of the parents had a cooler full of Coca-Cola products.

One of the dads came up as Frank was bagging the team's equipment. He said, "I hope it's not going to be like that for the next three months." Frank ignored him and walked past him toward his Chevy. One of the assistant coaches stepped in to defend how the team was preparing. When Frank was far enough away, he said under his breath, "Asshole."

Frank was mad, he was frustrated, he was confused, and he was disappointed as he approached his car. Then he looked up and saw Daniel standing beside the passenger's door, waiting on him. There was a smile across the little boy's face as he ate the M&Ms. Frank tried to smile back at him but just couldn't muster it.

"Daniel," he said, throwing the baseball equipment in his trunk, "we are going to McDonald's. I'll buy you supper. I may never go to Burger King again as long as I live." Daniel kept on smiling and got in the car.

⚾ ⚾ ⚾

The evening after that first scrimmage, Frank went to the recreation fields to watch two other teams involved in a scrimmage. He thought he might learn something or at least see the other league competition. Frank folded his arms across the top of the left field fence. He had not been there long when he felt a hand patting him on his shoulder.

It was Terry Thompson.

"Tough scrimmage last night," Terry said.

"You aren't kidding," Frank said. "I didn't know you could lose a baseball game that badly. We didn't have a chance."

Terry moved in to stand beside him. "It's a good thing what you are doing for little Daniel, helping him get to the practices. You will probably have to help him get to games too."

Frank was quiet and didn't want to talk right now. Terry could see he was stewing.

"Alright, look at me and listen to me," Terry said, sounding like a big brother. "I'm going to tell you something that almost every coach and parent out here has forgotten. If you listen to me, it's going to help you a lot."

Frank turned his head to look at Terry.

"This is not about baseball," he said, seriously and sternly, waving his left hand in a big circle to figuratively cover the entire ballpark. "It's not about baseball, winning or losing, or anything related to sports. We are out here serving, for the boys. It's about encouraging boys to be a part of something bigger than themselves. It's about loving them and caring about them and being their friend. Always remember, it's not about the baseball; it's about the boys."

"I'm not sure all the parents feel that way," Frank said.

"It doesn't matter," Terry said. "Be the kind of man that people want to see coming in their direction. Be the kind of man that boys look forward to seeing for the rest of their lives. At every practice, ask each of them how their day went, if school classes are going well, and encourage them to do their best. You may be the only person in their lives asking those questions. You'll be surprised at something. They will start playing better than they are physically equipped to play." He patted Frank on the shoulder and walked away.

Frank then heard Terry say behind him, "Bet you didn't eat Burger King last night." Frank smiled as he heard the laughter.

"You are right, I went to McDonald's," he shouted, and Terry Thompson threw his head back, laughing, but never looked back at him.

Frank continued to watch the two teams practice but didn't pay much attention to the game. He stood on that fence, thinking through every face on his roster and thinking how he could do a better job of encouraging them. He smiled, finally, and went to his Chevy.

⚾ ⚾ ⚾

The boys were sluggish at the next day's practice. They had thought they might be good, but the scrimmage with Burger King had been a reality check, and now doubts were creeping in. A few negative parents didn't help. Half the team had been on the league's worst team the year before, laughing stocks at school and church, and none of them wanted to be in that position again. Frank could sense that the parents attending practice weren't faring any better.

One of the dads threw batting practice, and Frank stood at third base, coaching and encouraging the defense as it played balls that were hit. He noticed that Joel kept having to stop and adjust or re-strap the catcher's gear shin guards. It kept slowing practice, and the boy was getting frustrated.

Further, Frank looked at the batting helmets. The foam protectant inside some of them was in pieces. Chin straps were dirty and old, and Frank was sure that several were from old football helmets.

After dropping Daniel at home that evening, Frank went for a fried chicken dinner at his favorite place in town. As he sat inside the restaurant, he thought of a high school basketball coach he had admired. As the local newspaper's sports reporter, Frank knew all the high school coaches well – as men and coaches, not just as teachers. Frank was impressed with the new basketball coach, who ensured his players had new equipment, an upgraded locker room, and the best possible uniforms.

"First class or no class," the coach said over and over again. "If you think and look like a champion, you'll play like a champion. If you look like you belong in the cheap seats, well, that's where you deserve to be."

Now, eating chicken, Frank thought of that coach and the mantra. He made a decision that night – a somewhat bold decision for a twenty-two-year-old transplant into this southeast Georgia community.

⚾ ⚾ ⚾

Frank sat in a large waiting room. Time was of the essence, and he didn't call ahead. Frank checked in at the newspaper and then left, driving to the ITT Rayonier paper mill. He parked in a large parking lot's "Visitors Only" spaces and walked into the main office. From there, he made his way to the office of the plant manager and corporate vice president.

Frank introduced himself as being on staff at the *Press* but made sure the plant manager knew he was not there representing the newspaper.

"What can I do for you?" the man asked, standing behind his desk and shaking Frank's hand across from it. He sat down again, sending a clear message that he was extremely busy and had just a few minutes for whatever was on this young man's mind.

"I'm coaching the recreational baseball team that is sponsored by the paper mill," Frank said. "That's why I'm here."

A smile crept across the plant manager's face, and he leaned back in his chair. He seemed glad this wasn't a surprise interview for the newspaper.

"Our team's equipment is terrible," Frank said. "The catcher's gear is falling apart, the batting helmets are old and shoddy, and I want this team to look good on the field. Last year, they were the worst in the league, and I just figure they need a boost in their confidence. I believe some new equipment will do it." He stopped and stared. "I was hoping the paper mill could buy the team some new equipment."

"How much do you need?" the man asked, leaning back in his chair.

"I can get what I need for $150," Frank said, handing over a piece of paper that listed all the items and a cost for each. "I'm going to Waycross on Saturday to buy what I need. I called them and priced everything. I want to get some baseballs, too, for practice. About half our baseballs are old." He had brought one with busted seams as evidence and held it for the man to see.

"Alright," the plant manager said. "Come back before 5:00 p.m., and I'll make sure we've got a check out there." He pointed to the lobby. "I'll have them make it out to you."

"Thank you, sir," Frank said. "We're going to have a team party at the end of the season, and I'll make sure you are invited to it. I want the boys to thank you personally. And you are welcome to come to all of our games. I'll make sure you have a schedule."

"Good luck this season," he said, standing again and shaking Frank's hand. "Thank you for what you are doing with these boys."

As Frank left the office, he heard the manager pick up his telephone and call the plant's business office.

⚾ ⚾ ⚾

The plant manager was better than his word. When Frank picked up the check, it was for $200 with a hand-written note, "Above all else, have fun." For a long time, Frank kept that note on his car's dashboard as a reminder.

On the way back to the newspaper office, he stopped by Daniel's house and asked the boy's mother if Daniel could ride to Waycross with him the next day, Saturday, to buy new baseball equipment for the team. He told her he would come by about 9:00 a.m., and she said she would have him ready to go.

Then Frank went to the newspaper office. He called Joel's house and spoke with his mom. He explained that he needed Joel to go with him to Waycross to try on new catcher's equipment, to make sure it fit him. She agreed that Joel could go and was relieved because her boy had bruises on his legs where balls hit him as the old shin guards shifted around on the worn straps.

To round things out, Frank called the parents of his shortstop, Billy. He thought that if the batting helmets fit Billy, Joel, and

Daniel, one or more of the helmets would fit all the boys on the team.

On Saturday morning, Frank rode around town picking up the three boys, talking to their parents, and then taking off for Waycross, an hour to the southwest. He promised to have them home by just after lunch and that he would buy them lunch too. Along the drive, Joel entertained them all with stories from school. Billy piped in when he could get a word in edgewise. Daniel simply smiled and looked out the window, soaking all of it in.

"Daniel, you don't say much, do you?" Joel asked him, not in a mean way, but just having fun.

Daniel smiled at him but didn't say anything. Frank wanted to tell Joel that over the past two weeks, he had never heard Daniel say a single word. He refrained from doing that because he felt Joel might worry the little boy to death.

Arriving in Waycross, the quartet walked into The Sports Stop, and the boys marveled at how big the store was and how it was dedicated solely to sports equipment of all kinds. Frank led them over to the store's left side, where all the baseball equipment was stacked and shelved.

"I need to buy this boy some catcher's gear," Frank said, taking Joel by the elbow and gently moving him toward a salesman. "He needs everything from shin guards up to his mask and helmet." After three attempts to get the right sizes, Joel stood there comically in the new gear. He got down in his catcher's stance.

"This feels so much better," he said. "Maybe I won't die back there."

Frank told the salesman that he also wanted six new batting helmets in varying sizes to fit the boys on his team. They followed the salesman to a large display, where helmets of varying colors were in large racks.

"I want the green ones," Frank said.

"Coach, that's going to look great," Billy said under his breath.

"It will be better than that blue . . ." Frank caught himself and said "crap" to finish the sentence.

It was easy to fit helmets for Joel and Billy, but there wasn't a green one small enough for Daniel – and Frank was pretty sure the second baseman, Chris, would need the smaller one too.

"I can sell you a smaller black one, and you can spray-paint it green," the salesman said. "You will need to put primer on it first, and then two or three coats of the green to match the others. It might not be a perfect match, but it will be close."

Frank took his advice and got one black helmet that he would paint the next day, Sunday, and Daniel and Chris could share it during practices and games.

"Is there anything else?" the man asked.

"Yes, I'd like twelve pairs of green stirrups," Frank said.

When giving out the uniforms, and in the first scrimmage, Frank noticed that the boys wore their white baseball pants with varying colors of socks, and he thought it just looked stupid. Some wore white socks, some wore white socks with red or blue rings at the top, and a boy named Ralph wore black socks that he surely wore for church too. When Frank saw the paper mill's extra money, he decided to upgrade each boy's uniform with stirrups to wear over white socks.

At the cash register, the total left about $20.

"I've got $200," Frank said, holding up cash from the check. "Can you throw in a box of good baseballs and make it an even $200 for everything?"

The salesman smiled, reached on a shelf, and pulled down a box of baseballs.

Within an hour, they were back in Frank's Chevy. Frank had one more idea.

"How would you all like some lunch?" he asked. "Let's get pizza." Frank intentionally looked in the rearview mirror at Daniel, who was still staring out the window, but Frank swore the little boy's smile was twice as big as it had been. It was a big deal to these boys, and Frank knew it: traveling with their coach on a mission to benefit the team and then having pizza like grown-ups on a business trip.

At the Waycross Pizza Hut, sitting at a four-seat table, Frank let the boys choose the toppings, but he warned them that they all had to eat whatever they ordered. So they were careful. When Daniel didn't offer up a topping suggestion, Frank pressed him.

"Hey, big guy," Frank said. "You have to pick a topping."

The smile on Daniel's little face vanished, and he bit his lip.

"I'm going to read the toppings to you, and you stop me when you hear one you want," Frank said. He began naming off meat toppings, and Daniel nodded his head when Frank said "hamburger." Frank winked at him and shook his head.

When the pizza came with four Cokes, Joel and Billy each grabbed a piece as Daniel hesitated.

"Boys," Frank said, "I was older than you before I had my first pizza in a restaurant like this. I was in high school and worked at a pizza restaurant." Daniel's eyes were as big as quarters. "I had to learn how to eat pizza. You guys grab a slice and let me show you. You hold it back here at the wide end and curl it just a little to hold it still. Then you start eating the pointed end like this." Frank took a bite and quickly chewed and swallowed. "But you can also just fold it over, so there's crust on both sides like this. Go ahead and try it."

Frank tried not to watch as Daniel folded the pizza slice and then ate it. He looked at Frank and smiled, and Frank then knew that all was well.

⚾ ⚾ ⚾

The next week, the ITT Rayonier boys played their second scrimmage and won over Tim's Body Shop and Transmission Repair, 10-6. Faris went four for four with two doubles, and the infield defense was stellar. After the game, Frank addressed the team as they sat on the dugout bench.

"You boys played well," he said, beaming. "You played baseball, and you had fun. The stirrups look great. Joel, how about that equipment?"

"Coach, I felt like a real catcher," he said. "I think my grown cousins wore that old equipment when they were my age."

"Some of you boys got on base tonight for the first time," Frank said. Daniel had walked, living up to Joel's prophecy that if the little boy just stood at the plate and didn't swing, he would always get on base.

Frank congratulated each boy as he left the dugout and gave each boy a pack of M&Ms.

Mark, the third baseman, took his pack of candy and then held it up to Frank and said, "I like you, Coach. Keep the candy coming."

"Keep making those plays, Mark," Frank said. "You played great over there. You won't have many plays at third, but we need you to make every play that comes your way. We can't win without you. If a ball gets by you to the fence, the runners will be on a race track for home.

⚾ ⚾ ⚾

The next day, Frank was at work when he took a telephone call from Terry Thompson, who asked him to drop by his office. Frank didn't think much of it. The recreation department was always calling the newspaper in need of publicity for its activities or events.

Frank walked into Terry's office and knew that something wasn't right.

"Did you go out to the paper mill and get $200 for new baseball equipment?" Terry asked him.

"Yes," Frank said, sensing aggravation from the recreation director. "What's the big deal?"

"The big deal is that we already get a few hundred dollars from each of our team sponsors, including the paper mill," Terry said. "We use a part of that money for baseballs, equipment, and uniforms. Not only did you ask them for additional money, kind of under the table, but you also told them the equipment we are using is shoddy."

"I know the plant manager didn't complain," Frank said. "I know he didn't."

"No, he didn't," Terry said. "But your opponent the other night asked how you all suddenly had brand-new catcher's equipment,

61

matching helmets, and stirrups that no other team in the league has. I asked around and found out you got money from the paper mill and took off to Waycross on a shopping spree."

"Terry, I'm sorry," Frank said. "I should have thought it through. I'll call the plant and apologize."

"No," Terry said. "It's all water under the bridge now, but I want you to see that when you are in a community league like this, you have to be part of that larger league team too. As adults, we all have to be on the same page."

Frank wanted to debate that the league's equipment was terrible and embarrassing, especially when this league fed a very successful high school baseball program. Instead, he kept his mouth shut, accepting the hollow win that came with the new equipment, and left Terry's office.

⚾ ⚾ ⚾

Once it began, it was a great season. The team's pitching held up well, and Faris, the team's pitcher and shortstop, headed toward an extended summer of All-Star baseball through the state's recreation system. Every boy on the team had a game or games that featured a meaningful hit, runs scored, and a play in the outfield.

Though Daniel – and two others – only played sparingly on defense, the little boy learned to stop ground balls in the outfield and throw them in to shortstop or second base. Frank smiled when it happened, and especially that other boys went out of their way to quietly say, "Good play out there." Daniel smiled. By no means had Daniel become a chatterbox, but Frank would catch the occasional whisper of one or two words in response to a question.

Riding home from the recreation complex one day, Frank asked Daniel if he was looking forward to school being out for the summer. Looking out the window, Daniel said, ever so quietly, "Yes."

"What do you do during the summers off from school?" Frank asked.

"Fish," Daniel said. "I like to read too."

"Daniel, when I was about your age, I read all the time, especially during the summer," Frank said. "I would try to read ten books every summer." Daniel looked at him and held up five fingers.

"I like to read five," he said.

Frank was so thrilled to have a conversation with the little boy that he said, "I think five books in a summer is great. If I give you a baseball book, will you read it this summer?" Daniel smiled and nodded his head and then turned back to the window.

The boys were winning as much as they lost, and as the season drew down to its final game, Frank could not have scripted a better opponent for the finale than Burger King.

⚾ ⚾ ⚾

It was the last game of the season, and Frank addressed his team away from the parents and the fans. The team's record was 8-7, and they had been competitive in most of the losses. Considering the preseason thumping by Burger King, Frank thought his experimental season at coaching was a success.

"Boys," he said, "no matter how this game comes out, I'm proud of the way you've played this year, and I hope you've had as much fun as I have." He looked at their faces, one by one, and smiled. "If we beat Burger King, we'll have a winning season. Even if we lose to them, we will have won as many as we lost – it won't be a losing season, and you won't finish in last place."

Heads nodded. "And you'll still have M&Ms for us after the game," Mark, the third baseman said, creating snickers.

"That's right, and, win or lose, I'm also buying hot dogs after this game," Frank said. "So we are going out there and playing our best, following the same game plan we've used all season, and whatever happens will happen."

There was no fairy tale ending.

Burger King won the game, ensuring its place at the top of the league standings.

But every boy on ITT Rayonier walked off the field that day feeling as if he had accomplished something. The final score was 6-4, and Frank's team had the tying run at second when the last out of the game was made. But probably the greatest moment of the game came in the fourth inning, and while it wasn't quite fitting for a storybook, it was close enough.

Three of the boys on the team only got one at-bat, the league minimum for substitutes, and Daniel was always one of those boys. Listening to his teammates, Daniel had learned to take advantage of his size. It was hard to throw the little boy a strike, and if he was patient and didn't swing, he most always walked and got on base. Batting toward the bottom, he scored several runs because he was on base when the big hitters like Faris, Joel, Billy, and David, the first baseman, came to bat.

In the fourth inning, with the score tied at 3-3, ITT Rayonier had two outs and nobody on base. As Daniel started to the plate for his at-bat, Frank called him over.

"I want you to try to hit it," he said. "Take at least one good swing and see what happens. You've been practicing for almost three months, and you hit some in practice. Let's take a swing today and see what happens."

Daniel stared at him and smiled. In that soft, almost deep voice, he whispered, "Okay."

With two balls and no strikes, Daniel swung and missed the next one. Frank chuckled and rolled his eyes when the little boy looked at him and smiled underneath the green batting helmet.

On the next pitch, Daniel swung again – to the shock of everyone – and there was the unmistakable ding of an aluminum bat meeting a rawhide baseball. The ball dribbled out to the right of the pitcher, just too far for an easy grab by the catcher or pitcher and not far enough for the third baseman. Baseball statisticians call it a "swinging bunt."

"Run," Frank shouted as if Daniel was on fire, and the little boy took off for first. "Run to me, Daniel. Run to me!" Those little legs were churning, and he got to the bag just as the ball did. Frank looked at the first base umpire, his eyes begging for Daniel to be called safe.

"He's safe!" the umpire shouted, and Frank breathed and looked to the sky as the team – players and parents – broke out in cheers for their undersized teammate. Daniel looked at them and smiled – big, big this time. Faris was up next, but before walking to the plate he trotted over to first and exchanged a hand slap with Daniel. Frank beamed at the sportsmanship.

Faris crushed the first pitch to the right-field gap. Daniel made it around to third, and Faris was safe at second with a stand-up double.

Billy was up next and flared a ball just out over the third baseman's head, and Daniel scored. The stands and dugout erupted again, and Frank gave him a hand slap as he walked to the dugout. Daniel had hit, run, and scored – Daniel was now a baseball player.

The inning ended with the next hitter grounding out to short. But for that brief moment, ITT Rayonier enjoyed a lead over vaunted Burger King, and little Daniel had scored the single most celebrated run of the season.

⚾ ⚾ ⚾

A week after the season was over, as the league's top four teams competed in a short playoff series, Frank called his team together for one last gathering – a cookout at a local park. Parents and siblings came with their favorite player, and it was quite a crowd.

Frank invited plant leadership from ITT Rayonier, and one of the plant manager's key executives came to the party. To the man's credit, he got there early, helped cook burgers and hot dogs, and then was one of the last to leave. He visited with every family.

After the picnic meal, Frank called everyone to be quiet, and one by one recognized each boy for their contributions to the team and then presented each one with a small trophy. Frank also had paper certificates for the team's oldest players, highlighting their statistical success over the season.

The executive from ITT Rayonier then applauded the team and made a short speech about the importance of being a part of something larger than yourself. The audience applauded.

Frank gave each boy their last pack of plain M&Ms, and then one of the parents got up and said, "Coach Frank, we have something for you." From a paper bag, she removed a large gallon-sized glass jar full of plain M&Ms. Everyone cheered. Another parent, who had ordered the boys trophies, gave Frank one of the trophies, and it was inscribed to him. Joel, the team's catcher, gave Frank a coffee cup with his name on it. Frank drank from that cup for more than two decades. He then retired it to a bookcase.

"Thank you all," Frank said. "I didn't know how this was going to go when I first agreed to it, but I will never forget this team and the success we had, especially improving over last season."

The boys played after the party was over, and then everyone cleaned up and started for their cars. Frank enjoyed spending time with Daniel's family, and they thanked him over and over for helping with their son's transportation. When Daniel asked if he could stay and play with the other boys, Frank agreed to bring him home.

"Frank," the man from ITT Rayonier said, "I want you to have this just to help with the expenses of tonight." He gave Frank a $50 bill and shook his hand. "Everyone expects dads to step up and coach teams. I think it says a lot for a single young man with family so far away to step up and do it."

"I enjoyed it," Frank said. "It gave me a distraction. If it had not been for this, I would have just gone home from work and watched television."

"Don't stop coaching," the man said, and again shook Frank's hand.

Frank and Daniel were the last to leave the park, and Frank drove him to Parkston Street for the last time. Turning into the driveway, Frank turned off the car. They got out, and Frank helped Daniel with his trophy and gifts.

"I've enjoyed spending time with you this season, Daniel," he said. "I hope you will play again next year."

Daniel didn't look at him but whispered, "Will you be my coach?"

"If I'm here, I will be," Frank said. "I don't know where I'll be in a year."

He walked with him to the porch and met Daniel's mother there.

"I've enjoyed coaching Daniel this year," Frank said. "I've got something for him."

From behind his back, Frank handed Daniel a paperback children's book about the great Hall of Fame outfielder, Willie Mays. Mays was still a relatively new Hall of Famer.

"Coach, I have something for you," the woman said, producing a homemade apple pie. "I hope you like apple pie. It's not much, but thank you again for helping with rides to the ballpark."

Frank took the pie and smiled.

"Come on, Daniel. You have homework," she said. The boy started up the porch steps, and Frank turned around and started back toward the car. He said without looking back, "Come see me at the newspaper office sometime, Daniel. It's not very far from here."

Frank was almost to the Chevy when he heard something startling, something he had not heard all season long.

It was a shout.

"Coach! Wait," the voice said, and Frank turned to see Daniel running toward him. The little boy threw his arms around Frank's right leg and didn't say anything else. He just held him tightly.

Frank got down on one knee, eye level to his player, and hugged him around the neck. He could feel Daniel gently crying even if he couldn't hear him.

"I know," Frank said. "It's hard saying good-bye, especially after all the fun we've had. You keep practicing, but mostly I want you to keep reading."

"I will," Daniel said in the customary whisper. Frank used his thumb to wipe tears from the little boy's eyes. Daniel smiled, turned, and walked back to the house, stopping on the porch steps and waving as Frank drove away.

Frank might have wiped tears from his eyes on the drive back to Cherry Street, but seven months later he was moved to smile. Driving a moving van out of Jenson, he saw Daniel crossing a street ahead of him. The little boy was proudly wearing his ITT Rayonier jersey.

⚾ ⚾ ⚾

After the first inning, the Braves and Marlins were scoreless.

Frank wrote Daniel's name at the top of the scorebook, thinking he might just take off one weekend to Jenson, Georgia, to see if he could find the boy or find his family.

Frank was snapped from his daydream by Bradley at the end of the row.

"You want a beer?"

"No, thanks," Frank said. "I still got some of this one," and pointed to the cup in his cup holder.

Phil jumped to his feet and handed money across Frank and Whitney, and Bradley took it. "Bring me one, please." He sat back down and leaned toward Frank. "It's gonna be a long game."

Frank was sure that good old Phil was right about that.

SECOND INNING
THE WEAPON

Down by the river, by the old cemetery
That's where the other team's gonna get buried
Six feet wide
Six feet under
When we fight, it sounds like thunder

The Braves ran onto the field for the second inning, and Phil said to no one in particular, "That Andruw Jones may be the best center fielder the Braves have ever had. He should go into the Hall of Fame one day."

"He's special," Frank said, still trying not to engage in a long conversation that would distract him from the game and his scorebook.

One of the little boys in front of Frank began waving a red foam tomahawk as part of the Braves "chop" that began during the worst-to-first season of 1991.

"He's so cute," Whitney, the young woman beside Frank, said while watching the little boy wave the red tomahawk. She looked to Bradley to see his reaction, and he shrugged his shoulders.

Phil had called attention to Andruw Jones, and Frank fixed on the Braves center fielder. Phil was right: Andruw Jones was a very special talent, especially on defense.

"It's pretty fantastic that the Braves have both Chipper Jones and Andruw Jones," the man just behind Frank said. "That Andruw is, for sure, a weapon. Fly balls go to center field to die."

Frank tried to tune them all out, patiently, just as he did when visiting the Concord Library's basement surrounded by people who wanted to talk out loud rather than whisper. He wrote the word "Weapon" at the top of the scorebook's page. That word took him back to his first season coaching in Stanton, Georgia – about seventy miles north of Jenson and an hour's drive west from Savannah.

⚾ ⚾ ⚾

Within six months of coaching the ITT Rayonier team in the Jenson Recreation League, Frank took a job as the associate editor of the *Herald*, a daily newspaper in the college town of Stanton, Georgia. It all happened fast. The Christmas after that first baseball season, Frank was invited to interview for the Stanton job, and within three weeks he was hired and on the ground working at the daily newspaper. As in Jenson, Frank knew no one in Stanton and once again had to bloom in a new place.

He rented one side of a new duplex located just off the college's campus and directly across the road from where a new football stadium was being built. The proximity to the campus allowed him to be around other twenty-somethings – even though he remained completely faithful to Vicki, who was still three hours away at the University of Georgia in Athens.

He found a smaller, friendly church just outside of the city limits. They were Presbyterians and made a "wayward Baptist" feel right at home.

The larger daily newspaper was a great work environment. Many young adults, like him, worked there, and that youthful environment kept the workday fun. After work, it was not unusual for a group to have dinner together, play racquetball, or meet at one of the college bars. Frank quickly realized that it wasn't working if you were having fun while you were there.

Working at the community's newspaper allowed reporters to get to know influential people in the community, and do so pretty quickly. While he was no longer writing sports, Frank was introduced to all the local recreation department staff. He first met Eddie Smart, who coordinated the department's youth sports programming, through one of those introductions. The introduction came at a men's league basketball game only a month after Frank moved to the community.

Some of Frank's peers on the newspaper staff had organized a basketball team, and while Frank didn't play basketball, he went to the local gym one night to watch his new friends play. Eddie Smart was there in an official capacity and to help work the game clock. At halftime, Frank introduced himself. That introduction led him to drop by the recreation department the following day, gathering press releases for publication in the newspaper. Eddie was his primary contact.

There was no receptionist on duty, and Frank cautiously followed the sounds of an office conversation down a long hallway. Coming to an open door, he saw Eddie sitting at a desk and another man, whom he had not met, leaning against a wall. Frank tapped lightly on the open door.

"Sorry to bother you," Frank said. "I dropped by to see if you all had anything for us at the newspaper."

"Yes, we do," Eddie said. "We are going to need some baseball coaches, and I need to put out the call through the newspaper and radio stations." He got up and pushed past Frank to an old file cabinet. There, Eddie took a three-page stapled document and gave it to Frank. "This is everything about the league this year, and you can see we need two more coaches in the ten to twelve age group."

Frank looked at the page. "I can help," he said.

The man leaning against the wall extended his hand and said, "Hi, my name is Randy Nixon. I'm the recreation director."

"Hi, I'm Frank Wilcox. I'm the new associate editor at the *Herald*."

"We appreciate you helping us," Randy said. Randy was kind, and asked Frank about his hometown, where he went to school, and how he came to be in Stanton.

Eddie called Frank's attention back to the document. "If you can make an article out of that information, it will help us out. If you can just let it run until we get everyone registered and coaches are certified, that will be great."

"Well, yes, we can do that," Frank said. "You say you need coaches? I can coach a team." Frank paused when he said it. It sounded like a foreign language coming from his lips. He sounded like a tenured coach, but the only team on his resume was the ITT Rayonier boys from Jenson.

Eddie grimaced. Randy's reaction was not as dramatic.

"I don't know," Randy said. "We've used younger guys before from the college." He paused. "You are pretty new to town and you probably have a lot going on while you get settled." It was a kind way of saying Frank had not been in town long enough for the recreation staff to really know him.

"I don't have a lot of distractions," Frank said. "I don't have family here; my girlfriend is in Athens, and then she will be visiting her family in Texas all summer. I'm not crazy about going to Savannah and the beaches. I coached last year in Jenson. You can call Terry Thompson down there if you need a reference."

"I know Terry," Randy said. "I may call him."

Frank didn't push the sales pitch. He smiled and said, "Well, if you need help coaching, please let me know. I'll be glad to volunteer." He took the league information and left, making his way back to the office.

⚾ ⚾ ⚾

Frank was busy settling into his work at the newspaper, meeting new people every single day, and adjusting to life in a busier city. He almost forgot about volunteering to coach baseball until his telephone rang one afternoon at work and Eddie Smart was on the other end of the line.

The short of it was that a team was available. If Frank wanted to coach, and had time, he could serve as the team's coach.

"I'm still a little cautious, but we need coaches, and Terry down in Jenson says you did a great job last season," Eddie said. "We're going to take a chance. I know that you don't know anyone here in Stanton, but do you think you might know anyone there at the newspaper who can help you?"

As Eddie spoke, Frank was staring across the room at his friend Mack. Mack had been the first hand he shook among his workplace peers on the first day of work, and it was Mack who introduced him to others and helped him find his way. Frank smiled.

"I'm pretty sure I can find help," Frank said, watching his new friend with the thick black hair and moustache entertain the newsroom with a story.

"Alright, I need you to drop by here and complete a coach's application," Eddie said. "Then I'll need you to attend two certification meetings. I can explain how our league works because it's probably a little different than the league in Jenson."

Before going to the recreation department and signing on to coach, Frank thought it wise to make sure he could enlist help. Mack agreed to help. Someone overheard his conversation with Mack and mentioned that Jane, a young woman who sold advertising, had been a great softball player in high school. Frank asked her to help, too, and at first, she laughed it off. After realizing he was serious, she also agreed to help.

⚾ ⚾ ⚾

Frank went to the recreation department and completed his application. He attended the certification classes and passed a simple test at the end. Eddie gave him a thirty-minute orientation about the league rules, practice expectations, and how the distribution of equipment was managed.

"When is the draft?" Frank asked, remembering the awkward formation of his team in Jenson.

"We don't have a draft," Eddie said. "The recreation staff invites all the players to a clinic. We take the players through some skills assessment, and then we put the teams together. Coaches and parents aren't involved. Rosters change every season. That's how we maintain parity within the league and keep everything fair."

It was perfect for someone like Frank, who didn't know anyone. He looked forward to getting his roster and getting practice underway. As he started to leave the meeting with Eddie, the league supervisor looked Frank in the eyes and, with a slight smile, said, "Your team is going to be the Stanton Lions. Don't go ask the Lions Club for money to buy new equipment."

Frank rolled his eyes, chuckled to himself, and walked out of the office. He could imagine Terry Thompson laughing about now too.

⚾ ⚾ ⚾

At a coach's meeting the following week, Eddie gave Frank his team roster. Randy was in the meeting, too, because he wanted to give Frank some insight into some of his players.

James was highlighted as a sure pitcher. He was one of the team's oldest, tallest, and most athletic players. "He'll be one of your team's All-Stars," Randy said.

"What about a catcher?" Frank asked, and Eddie pointed to Jeffrey on the roster sheet.

"He's a great kid," Eddie said. "He comes from a great family that will be completely supportive."

The two men went through the remainder of the roster, suggesting possible positions and who might get a look at pitching. Many of the boys had parents who were professors at the local college, and there was a strong connection between the recreation department and the college's athletics department.

"This one," Eddie said, pointing to the name John on the roster sheet, "I think he's a sleeper. When the season is over, I won't be surprised to see his name in All-Star conversations."

Randy leaned back in an office chair and put his hands behind his head. "I'm going to give you one piece of advice: be organized and communicate well. In my experience, the coach must be the most passionate person on the team – you must love this opportunity more than any player or parent involved. If you are fully invested, it calms everyone down. What upsets parents is that no one is in charge and they aren't in the loop of information. As a young man, you will need to be organized and communicate well to earn respect."

"I hope the players love it the most," Frank said.

"I want the players to have a great experience, and they will if you fully embrace this opportunity to serve," he said.

Frank left the meeting full of confidence, looking forward to calling the players that evening and inviting them to the team's first practice the following Saturday.

⚾ ⚾ ⚾

The first practice was at the Jaycee Field just behind the recreation department, which was located at the convergence of two main traffic arteries into Stanton. Frank gathered his team together, and parents stood around behind them. Eddie Smart insisted on being at the meeting, especially since Frank was a new coach. Frank was thankful to have him there.

Frank first introduced Mack and Jane, and having a female coach got everyone's attention. Jane never flinched over whether she belonged or not, and the preadolescent boys seemed perfectly happy to have her there. Frank was glad to have her there, too, because she had played far more organized ball than he and Mack combined.

Frank went over the league rules, especially regarding game management and playing time. He made it clear that not everyone would get to play every inning and that some hitters would share a place in the batting order.

"If you work hard, come to practices, and get better, I'll make sure you have at least one game where you get to play the entire game without a substitute," he said. "Other than that, we are playing to win." He pointed to the scoreboard in left field. "The scoreboard will be turned on during our games."

Parents nodded their approval though Frank knew every single one of them thought their boy was worthy of never having a substitute. It was going to be a shock for some of them.

"I have one more important rule to share," Frank said. "It's in article III, section A, number 1 of the local rule book. The players stared at him, and the parents stared even harder. Frank maintained a poker face as he further read, "Shoes are mandatory for play in boys baseball games."

It took a minute, but everyone laughed. Frank held up a printed page to prove it was in the rules. There would be no bare-foot baseball, which there had been at one time or another, necessitating the rule.

Frank went on to say that he needed two dollars for every player because he would make sure they had royal-blue stirrups to match their T-shirt jerseys and hats. He also told them that there would be a cookout at the end of the season, and the team would celebrate whatever kind of season it had.

From there, Frank Wilcox began his first practice with the members of the Stanton Lions Club baseball team. As with his Jenson team, he started with defensive warm-ups and took infield as he and the coaches scouted possible player positions. He incorporated batting practice into a scrimmage that involved some of the dads helping out in the outfield. Frank had learned one thing in Jenson: the boys loved playing the game, and having a pickup game at each practice made the practices fun. Those chosen last were the team captains at the next practice.

Eddie Smart had walked back to his office at the department rather than be on hand during practice, but as Frank finished up and approached his car, Eddie met him there.

"Looks like a good start," he said.

"It's going to be a fun year," Frank said. "Win or lose, it's going to be fun."

⚾ ⚾ ⚾

At the team's second practice, Frank began to try boys at different positions, hoping to set his infield as quickly as possible. A preseason scrimmage loomed large, and Frank didn't want to waste the chance to see boys playing at specific positions.

For all the help with player evaluation that he received from Eddie and Randy, the men overlooked a player named Clinton. Even at the first practice, it was clear Clinton had exceptional defensive skills, and regardless of where Frank put him on the field, the boy made plays.

At the second practice, Frank asked him to play third base, which Mack felt was a misuse of the boy's talent.

"Clinton needs to be at short," Mack said. "Move John to third. We will be solid as a rock on the left side of the infield."

"I don't know," Frank said. "I think John covers more ground at short, and I think he instinctively knows what to do with the ball. Clinton can handle anything hit to third – no matter how hard it's hit. It will be the same result – we will be rock solid over there."

"Your call then," Mack said, and then shouted to the players, "Let's warm up those arms." He clapped his hands and walked among the players.

The Lions blistered the Civitan team in that first preseason scrimmage. While the score was not officially kept, Frank knew his boys had won 15-5, and could have won by even more, but the Civitan coach called the game after the fourth inning.

In the third inning, Clinton dropped to a knee and fielded a three-hop rocket down the third base line, catching the ball right in front of his face. He then jumped back to both feet and threw a lazy ball over to first for the out.

A noticeable sigh came from both sides of the bleachers as everyone realized what a remarkable play had just been made by a twelve-year-old on the Jaycee field.

"That kid is special," Mack said, turning to Frank.

Clinton was the first player in a lengthy line of players to receive a nickname from Frank.

"Magic Hands," Frank said. "I'm going to start calling him Magic Hands."

"Appropriate," Mack said. "I'm glad I don't have a sister his age." Jane overheard it and shoved him, shaking her head with a frown. Rubbing his shoulder, he said, "Okay, we'll just call him Magic."

⚾ ⚾ ⚾

Frank was sitting at his kitchen table, eating a plate of spaghetti when he received the telephone call. Clinton was out for the season.

"Coach, I'm sorry," the timid woman's voice said on the telephone. "Clinton has broken his wrist. He was on the trampoline and bounced off, and just landed funny. We just got home from the emergency room, and he's in a cast up to his elbow."

Frank pushed away the spaghetti, leaving a stream of Ragù sauce on the table. He had lost his appetite. Frank had broken his wrist on two different occasions while in high school. Frank knew Clinton would not be playing baseball this season. The season was too short, and the recovery was too long.

"I'm sorry too," Frank said. "I was looking forward to watching him play this year. He's got a special talent."

"He'll be back next year," she said. "His daddy is just glad this isn't happening before football season."

Frank called Mack and simply said, "Well, we need a third baseman. Our boy Magic Hands has broken his wrist."

⚾ ⚾ ⚾

The team's next practice, a Saturday morning, was across town at Blitch Field, which was part of the Luetta Moore Park, near an apartment complex. Frank was allowed two weeknight practices each week, one at the Jaycee field and the other at the Blitch field, and a third practice on Saturday morning. Wednesdays and Sundays were off-limits so that those wanting to attend church services could do so.

There was a warm breeze in the air that morning when Frank gathered the team together at Blitch Field. He shared the news about Clinton, and most of the boys already knew.

Freddie, a salty boy with a sharp tongue, said, "Dang, Clinton. I told him to stay off that stupid trampoline."

"Were you there?" Frank asked him.

"I was there," Freddie said. "He's been flirting around with one of the neighbor girls, and she was jumping, so he climbed on the trampoline with her."

There was some laughter among the older boys, and Mack looked at Frank and held up his hands as if to say, "I'm glad I don't have a sister his age."

Frank waved his hands so that the chatter would stop. "Let's warm up," he said. "Find a partner and start throwing."

Alex, an outfielder, asked, "Hey, is this field really called 'the Blitch'?"

Several of the older boys began snickering among themselves.

"Don't say it," Jane said firmly. She was wearing sunglasses, but Frank was pretty sure her eyes were burning through poor Freddie. He dropped his head and apologized.

That encounter caused snickering among all the boys because rarely did someone gut punch Freddie like that. Frank stepped in and barked at them to focus on practice.

"Everybody grab a position you've played before," he said. "Let's get going. We have to find a new third baseman."

Frank was hitting balls to the infield while Jane patrolled among the team, offering suggestions. Frank was proud of her for taking this opportunity, and he was proud of the way the boys respected her. They learned pretty quickly, watching her throw the ball around during warmups, that she knew a lot about the game. Mack was in the outfield, hitting fly balls to the five players out there. His encouraging and fun attitude was likely to create problems for Frank – everyone would want to play in the outfield and spend time with Coach Mack. There was no accounting for his value to the team.

Frank was focused on the infield practice when Chess ran in from the outfield and did not stop until he reached the head coach. Frank put the bat on his shoulder. "What's up?" he asked.

Panting, Chess said, "Coach Mack needs you for a minute," he said.

⚾ ⚾ ⚾

Unbeknownst to Frank, Charles, a tall athletic boy, had gotten up early that morning and walked outside the family apartment to ride his bike. He heard laughter – boys' laughter – from the nearby baseball field. With nothing else to do, he climbed on the bike and rode in the direction of the baseball field that was just inside the park.

When he could see the boys running and playing in the outfield, he stopped just beyond their ability to see him. It looked like fun – so much fun. He had played a little stick ball around the apartment complex, and regularly shot basketball at the park. It might be fun to spend a Saturday morning playing baseball with these boys. He didn't have a baseball glove, but maybe these boys had one he could borrow.

Boldly, he pedaled the bike up to the center field fence and sat there, watching Mack hit balls to a small group of players just on the other side of the fence. He watched the boys and figured he was at least as good a player as they were. He dropped the bike to the ground and approached the fence.

"Excuse me," he said. "Can I play?"

That's when Mack sent Chess to fetch Frank.

⚾ ⚾ ⚾

Frank walked toward the outfield, handing the bat to Jane so she could continue the infield practice. He approached Mack, who half whispered, "There's a boy on the other side of the outfield fence, and he's asking if he can play with us."

Frank took a big sigh. His team had a two-hour slot for practice, and he didn't need distractions. He walked out to the outfield fence, and through it saw a tall, slender boy with a serious stare – an all-business stare.

"What's up?" Frank asked.

"Can I come over and play?" the boy asked. His voice was full of confidence, and he looked Frank directly in the eyes as he spoke.

"This is a recreational team, and I can only let registered players come to our practices," Frank said. "If you are on another recreational team, you can come play, but just for today. Your coach might not like you practicing with us."

"No, sir, I'm not on a team," he said politely. "I just want to play."

"Have you ever played baseball?" Frank asked.

"No, not on a real team," he said. "I've just played around the neighborhood." He pointed to the apartments.

"What's your name?"

"Charles."

"Charles, I can't let you practice with the team," Frank said. "If you get hurt or if you accidentally hurt someone – you accidentally hit them with the ball – then I will get in big trouble."

The boy shrugged his shoulders and kept staring. He wasn't backing down. Awkward silence filled the air, and Frank spoke again.

"I can't invite you to jump that fence and play," Frank said. "If you choose to jump that fence, try to be invisible." He turned and started back toward practice, saying to Mack, "If he jumps the fence, let him shag some balls."

"Coach," he heard the boy's voice behind him, "I can't be invisible. I'm the only black person on this field." Frank laughed to himself but didn't look back as he walked toward the infield. Charles had already jumped the fence. Mack surrendered his glove for Charles to use.

For the rest of his life, Frank would not forget what happened next.

After a few more minutes of separately practicing the infield and outfield, Frank shouted to Mack to spread out the boys in the outfield. It was time to connect the outfield and the infield, so the two units knew how to play and work together during the game.

Frank expected Mack to send Charles to the fence to watch, but instead, Mack stood beside the team's practice guest in center field.

"Hey, Frank," Mack shouted. "Hit one out here."

Frank didn't want to do it. He did not want to hit a fly ball to a boy who had never played organized baseball. But he did anyway. The ball jumped off the bat and lifted toward center field, directly at Charles.

"Oh snot," Frank thought. "What have I done?" He tried to will the ball away from the boy, but Charles immediately threw his glove up in self-defense. Frank knew – deep down – that he would have to quit his job at the newspaper and leave town if this boy were injured.

It was awkward and not at all clean, but Charles caught the ball to the side of his head. Frank breathed a sigh of relief. He saw Mack lean toward the boy and whisper something, and it was then that Charles threw the ball.

The distance from center field to where Jeffrey, the Lions' All-Star catcher, was standing at home plate was about two hundred feet. Everyone, including Frank, expected Charles to lob the ball in to James, who was at short, and then James would relay the back ball back in to Jeffrey.

That did not happen.

Charles, oh he who had never played baseball before, unloaded a frozen rope from deep center field. It traveled on a straight line and popped into Jeffrey's mitt at home plate. The pop of the baseball hitting the glove was so intense that several of the infielders gasped and then yanked their heads in the direction of center field.

"Wow," Frank said barely above a whisper, but his catcher heard it.

"Amen, Coach," Jeffrey said.

The practice continued, and though it was against every league rule and possibly several legal insurance statutes, Charles finished that practice with the Lions. It was obvious to all that while Charles was rough around the baseball edges, he was already one of the team's best players. Defensively, he wasn't strong, but Charles seemed to have the tools to be a good hitter. He could also run with the wind, and, boy, oh boy, could he throw.

Walking to their cars after practice, Mack said, "Coach, we got ourselves a weapon."

"I have to figure out a way to get him on our team," Frank said.

Charles, the Weapon, was the second player Frank Wilcox ever offered a nickname.

⚾ ⚾ ⚾

On Monday afternoon, not appearing too anxious, Frank dropped by the recreation department and found Eddie Smart in his office.

"Anything I can take back to the newspaper?" Frank asked.

"Yes, here you go," Eddie said, handing Frank a short, type-written announcement for a senior adult ladies' hearts tournament.

"Eddie, you ever attend one of these hearts tournaments?" Frank asked.

"Nope," Eddie said without looking up from his desk.

"My hunch is that it's a cover-up for gambling," Frank said, laughing.

"No comment," Eddie said.

Frank changed the subject.

"Eddie, I've lost Clinton for the season," Frank said. "He's got a broken hand, and I'm going to need a replacement if you want me to carry a full roster."

"I'll take a look at late registration and call you later with a name," Eddie said without looking up.

Frank cleared his throat. "I've got a boy who would like to play baseball, and I can add him to make up that spot."

"Here we go," Eddie said, leaning back in his chair, which was more and more a position these recreation folks took as a defensive posture. Terry had done it in Jenson, and now Eddie was doing the same thing in Stanton. "You can't go fill your roster spots. We have a waiting list, and we assign players. That's how we keep the teams balanced."

"Hear me out," Frank said. "We were practicing on Saturday at Blitch, and this boy walked up from the neighborhood. He watched us practice, and he asked if he could play on our team. I told him that we did have a spot open and that I would check with you."

Eddie closed his eyes and stared at the ceiling. Frank was sure he heard a moan.

"To be honest, Eddie, he's not played before," Frank said. "He even told me that. He's not at all the defensive player that I had in Clinton. I hit him a few ground balls to see how they compare."

Randy appeared at the door, and Eddie filled him in. Randy grimaced.

"This could open up all kinds of problems, Frank," Randy said. "We don't let coaches recruit players. I'm sorry, and Eddie will agree with me. We can't do it." He left the office.

"You can still invite that boy to sign up," Eddie said. "If you really care about him playing. I can probably find a team for him – just probably won't be your team."

Frank wanted to argue but didn't. He left the office, knowing the right thing to do was find Charles and open the door for him to play in the league.

⚾ ⚾ ⚾

Finding the tidy apartment where Charles lived was not a problem; Frank recognized the bicycle beside the front door. Introducing himself and stepping inside, Frank breathed deeply and drew in the delicious smell of whatever was being cooked in the kitchen.

Charles's mother signed the registration form and promised to take her son's birth certificate and a check for the registration the next day. Frank passed along an information packet and told her that Eddie would assign Charles to a team. She said that her older son had plenty of sports equipment Charles could use.

"He plays a lot of basketball," she said, patting her son on the arm. "But this will be his first time on a baseball team."

"He's going to be just fine," Frank said. "I wish they would put him on my team."

⚾ ⚾ ⚾

Frank made it back to the recreation department just before 5:00 p.m. that day and gave Ed all Charles's paperwork. He started to argue for Charles to be on his team, but didn't. He respected the system, and he was new to it anyway. He also trusted Eddie to find a talented replacement for Clinton.

As Frank walked out of the office, Eddie said, "I appreciate you helping that young man."

Frank didn't turn around, but he thought, "Yep, I hope he does well against every team but mine."

⚾ ⚾ ⚾

At the next practice, Frank was in the dugout, waiting on players at the Jaycee field, when Eddie walked out of the recreation department office and approached him at the field.

"I've got a player for you, Frank," he said, giving a casual wave of the paperwork in his right hand. "Here's all of his contact information." He sat down by Frank in the dugout, handing him the paperwork.

Frank looked at it and then looked at Eddie. There was a smile on Frank's face.

"You sure he's never played before?" Eddie asked.

"I asked him about it, and he said he has never played before," Frank said. "His mama confirmed it. I've never seen him play in a game, and even in practice, he's not hit live pitching from another boy."

"Alright," Eddie said. "I hope it works out." He paused. "For all of us."

When Mack arrived at the field, Frank walked up to him and whispered, "We got our weapon." Mack slapped him on the back.

⚾ ⚾ ⚾

The Lions had two more preseason scrimmages. Eddie Smart was there to watch.

In the first scrimmage, Charles played the entire game at third base. He made the routine plays there, and for that Frank was glad. In four at-bats, he hit a single, walked, and drilled two home runs over the center-field fence. He scored three runs.

After the second home run, Frank sheepishly looked to where Eddie Smart had been sitting and saw the sports director's back as he walked toward the parking lot. Frank was pretty sure Eddie would never speak to him ever again.

In the second scrimmage, the Weapon hit one more home run.

Charles was 15-31 – a .483 batting average during that magical season – with two more home runs. He also helped pitch the team to a 10-2 record and a second-place finish in the league.

At the close of the season, the team's year-end cookout was at a community center near Blitch Field, where Charles had first appeared in center field. Frank gave each of the boys a baseball with their year-end stats written on it. When the party was over, several of the boys ran to the outfield of Blitch Field to play while their parents cleaned up.

Frank watched them run around, playing a game of chase, when Mack came up beside him. "The Weapon," he said, watching the boys at play.

"It was a fun year," Frank said. "You think he'll keep playing?"

"I sure hope so," Mack said. "If he ever gets real coaching, he could be dangerous." Frank smiled at the joke.

Charles's family was now leaving the party, walking toward the apartments behind the field. Someone called for Charles to join them, and he obediently grabbed his souvenir baseball and a bag of candy provided by the team mom. Just as he had joined the Lions, he left the same way.

He jumped over that center field fence and was gone.

⚾ ⚾ ⚾

After two innings, the Braves and Marlins were still scoreless.

"I'm cold," Whitney said to Bradley as she tried to snuggle closer to him despite the stadium seating's armrest between them.

"You want me to buy you a sweatshirt?" he asked her.

"No, I'll be fine," she said, and Frank so wanted to lean over to the young man and say, *"Bradley, you dumbass, go buy her a sweatshirt — no matter what she says, buy her a Braves sweatshirt."*

"I'm not eavesdropping," Frank said, "but I'm happy for you to wear this jacket if you are cold." He handed her the folded light jacket he had brought. "It's clean." He laughed.

She smiled at him, thankfully, and in her smile, Frank knew she wasn't nearly as pretentious as maybe her perfectly styled ensemble indicated she might be.

Frank pushed it into her personal space and said, "I wore layers. I won't need it, and I'd like you to be comfortable."

"Thank you," she said. She stood to put on the jacket, and Frank felt all the sales guys' eyes to his right, looking at her.

"Whitney and Bradley," Frank said, smiling. "You two have perfectly matched names."

She smiled. "We are getting married in the fall."

"Congratulations," Frank said. He told her about his wife, Vicki, and how they had visited Braves games on many occasions during their dating and engagement years. He told Whitney specifically about having a flat tire in the parking lot of nearby Grant Park Zoo, causing them to be late to one of the many games they attended.

The Braves were running on the field; Frank turned his attention to the game.

THIRD INNING
SAM

Sam's up to bat, Sam's up to bat
If I were you and you were me
I'd scoot my booty back – way back!

One of the little boys in front of Frank stood up and stretched. He turned to his brother and said, "I'm going to hit a home run this summer."

The other boy, who was sitting, said, "You are not," and a friendly back-and-forth began.

"You boys playing baseball this summer?" Phil, the salesman, asked them.

"They are playing All-Star baseball this summer," the dad said. "That one is a big talker." He reached over and flicked the standing boy's hat off his head. It dropped to the concrete but just as easily could have landed in the row in front of them.

"I am going to hit a home run this summer," the boy said indignantly.

"We'll see about that," the man said, shaking his head. "You are a big talker."

Phil said, "Believing in yourself is a big part of it. That and keeping your eyes on the ball."

"It's largely luck," the man in front said. "If they go up there wanting to hit a home run, they probably won't. Conditions have to be perfect. Every homer I've ever seen surprised the hell out of the hitter."

Frank shrugged his shoulders. He wasn't sure that was absolutely true, but he didn't want to start a debate. He just smiled. There was no getting around eavesdropping at a Braves game, and it all caused him to think of Sam.

⚾ ⚾ ⚾

Few boys loved baseball more than Sam — a chatty brown-haired eleven-year-old with wide eyes and a constant grin. He wasn't particularly athletic on the baseball field, but Frank noticed that players seemed to respect Sam for what he could do in other sports, like swimming.

When Frank first took over the Stanton Lions baseball team, he assigned positions based on recommendations from Eddie Smart and his staff at the recreation department. Like Sam, many of the boys came with no recommendation on position, and for these boys, Frank, Mack, and Jane had to find a place using trial and error.

Frank started Sam in the outfield, and in the two preseason scrimmages, he did well there. He caught fly balls, used his speed to run down balls on the ground, and had a decent arm when throwing the ball back into the infield. Sam's outfield work was short-lived. In the two scrimmages, against real competition, the coaches realized their initial pick to play first base was piling up errors. Frank moved Sam to first on Jane's suggestion, and immediately the infield defense snapped into place. Having Sam's chatty personality at first encouraged everyone in the infield. He kept everyone loose.

At the plate, however, Sam slumped terribly.

"Sam's a free swinger," Mack said over a beer after practice one evening. "He reminds me of myself in adult softball. 'Let's go down swinging!' is my motto. He's all over the place. It doesn't matter where the ball is; he's taking a hack at it."

"He's way out in front," Frank said. "When he does make contact, sometimes accidentally, he jerks it hard down the left field line. I've never seen a ten-year-old boy pull the ball with such force. I don't know that we can fix that in a single season."

At one practice, Sam had jerked a line drive down the left field line, foul, and into a small park. It had one-hopped an older woman right on her rear end and then still had enough bounce to hit a kid on a playground see-saw.

It caused quite a stir among the boys at practice, and Freddie shouted, "You kinda butt slapped that old gal, Sammy boy." Once again, Freddie got a lecture from Jane.

"Sam's a great kid though," Mack said. Shrugging his shoulders in consolation, he reminded Frank of his childhood friend Wendell Mann saying, "She's not real pretty, but she's got a great personality."

⚾ ⚾ ⚾

With Charles's addition to the team, the Lions had a lot of pop in the middle of their lineup. Charles and Jeffrey, the catcher, and James all had home run power, and each had at least one home run in the early days of the season. When that trio didn't hit homers, it was not unusual for them to hit the ball hard to the outfield. The surprise hitter of the season was John, who, like Sam, was quiet and unassuming. John and Sam were good friends.

Through the first three games of the season, John had one hit and was hitting at the bottom of the lineup. He had emerged as a solid pitcher alongside James and Charles and made every play at shortstop, though, at first glance, his athleticism might have been overlooked. While Mack lamented yet another strong fielder with no offensive game, Frank saw it all differently.

"John is solid and strong," Mack said. "It's a shame he can't hit well."

"I want to show you something about him," Frank said, throwing open his scorebook on the hood of his car. "It's in the stats and trends. John may not have had a hit in the first three games, but he's walked five times and only struck out once. This kid's a hitter, Mack, and he's going to start hitting. Right now, he's just patiently waiting on the pitches to hit. The numbers never lie."

Mack wasn't convinced, but Frank left his sure-handed shortstop in the lineup without a substitute. In game four, John started hitting. Over the next five games, he was 9-10 at the plate, a stunning .900 batting average that propelled him into being the team's best hitter by the end of the season.

As John got hot at the plate and excelled, his friend Sam wilted. It was becoming more difficult for the team's enthusiastic first baseman to keep that effervescent smile on his face.

As Frank gathered equipment following one of the team's practices, he heard a quiet voice speak to him, "Coach?" All the other boys had disappeared to their cars, and only Frank and Mack remained in the dugout.

Frank looked up to see Sam, whose shoulders were slumped in defeat.

"Hey, buddy, what's wrong?" Mack asked, sitting beside him on the dugout bench.

"I can't hit," Sam said. "Maybe I shouldn't play baseball."

"Keep working hard," Mack said, but Frank knew those encouraging words were a false salve for the broken spirit of his first baseman.

"I'm not doing anything Saturday morning if you want to work on your hitting," Frank said. "Ask your dad if he can bring you out here on Saturday morning."

"Okay," Sam said.

"Tell your dad to bring his glove," Frank said. "He will need to help us."

As Sam's smile returned, he turned and ran out of the dugout.

Mack looked at Frank. "You think you can help him?"

Frank breathed deep.

"Mack, you are looking at the worst hitter to ever walk on a baseball field," Frank said. "I have no idea how to help someone improve their hitting."

⚾ ⚾ ⚾

The following day, Frank dropped by the recreation department and tapped on Eddie Smart's open door before stepping inside. Ed looked up and rolled his eyes.

"I need some help," Frank said.

"Of course you do," Eddie said, smiling. "But no new players."

"No," Frank said. "I want to help this kid with his hitting, but I don't know very much about hitting."

Eddie leaned back in his chair, which now made Frank laugh to himself.

"I'm not sure a player can correct his hitting in a single season," Eddie said. "Most of these boys get by on natural ability – if it's there."

"I know," Frank said. "It's just that this one, Sam, wants to improve his hitting so badly, and I hate to tell him he's just got to settle with what the Lord gave him."

"Does he hit in practice?" Ed asked.

"He loves to swing," Frank said. "He misses a lot of balls, and when he does make contact, he pulls it hard to the left – usually foul." Frank sighed. "Yes, he strikes out a lot."

Eddie got up and left his office, and when he returned, he had Barry, another staff member, with him. Barry threw a rubber home plate onto the floor and stood beside it as a right-hander might.

"If he's pulling everything," Barry said, "you need to slow those hands down. Get him a heavier bat, for one, and then have him work on patience. Have him watch balls longer. You might have to adjust his feet in the batter's box so he's not opened up toward the left field foul pole." Barry demonstrated. "You can also move him up in the box, closer to the pitcher, so he keeps balls in fair play."

Frank was amazed. He had not expected to get real baseball instruction.

He grabbed a sheet of paper from Eddie's desk and began making notes to himself. As he wrote, Eddie said, "Don't discount the encouragement you can give him. He may just need a boost in his confidence."

"He's a big part of the team mix," Frank said. "He's always excited to be out there, and it rubs off on others. He's also a great first baseman. I just want to help him."

"I've said so many times," Eddie said, again leaning back in his chair with his hands now behind his head, "the secret to team coaching is to coach from the bottom up."

Frank stared at him.

"Every team has three to four God-gifted players," Eddie said, holding his hand up as high as possible. "Even if they aren't natural talents, they've got a support system at home that helps them get better. They've got brothers, dads, or uncles who were ballplayers. Many recreational coaches just lean or overlean on their talented players and hope they get a contribution from the others.

"I've always argued that if you want to build a great team, even in rec ball, you identify the boys who have the tools, who have the desire, but just need someone to bring it out in them," Eddie said. "If you can have three to four natural athletes" – he held his hand high again, and then lowered it – "and then another three to four players who are improving, well, now you've got a lineup with six to eight players who can make things happen."

"Right, but there's always that bottom third," Frank said.

Eddie smiled as if Frank was on the cusp of generational wisdom. He now leaned forward and put his hands on his desk. "Coaching isn't just managing what you got; it's improving what you got.

"That bottom four," Eddie said, tapping his finger on his desk, "that's where you win championships. Put in extra time with them.

Push them a little harder in practice. Pair them up with a better player. If those bottom four can improve just a little, well, added to the other eight – the stars and almost-stars – you'll have a great team."

Frank sat down.

"I'm meeting Sam and his dad on Saturday to work on Sam's hitting," Frank said.

Barry smiled, and Eddie shrugged his shoulders. "I think you are figuring it out, my young grasshopper." He winked at Frank.

"I may have figured it out, but we'll see if I can make it work," Frank said.

"Next year," Eddie said, "start the season off by identifying the players who need you the most. Try to see how much you can improve them throughout the season. That's what coaching is all about. It's not about sitting around watching your best players do their thing."

Coach from the bottom up. Frank never forgot the lesson that day.

⚾⚾⚾

On Saturday morning, Sam and his dad were waiting on Frank to arrive at the Jaycee field.

Frank opened his scorebook and sat by Sam on the bottom seat of the first base bleachers.

"Sam," he said, "in the first game against Kiwanis, you hit one time and struck out."

"Is this like a report card?" Sam asked him, leaning into Frank so he could see the pages.

"Kinda like that," Frank said. "In the second game, you hit the ball, but both times it went down here to third base. What we want to do is get you hitting the ball out here." Frank pointed toward the gap in left field.

"I got a good hit against Rotary," Sam said when Frank flipped the page.

"You did, but again, it was right down the left field line," Frank said. "You also struck out in the third inning."

"Why do I have to share one of the batting spots with Robbie?" Sam asked.

Frank breathed deeply, and Sam's daddy interjected for the first time. "Don't hold back, Coach; be honest with him." Frank nodded that he understood.

"Sam, your hitting is just inconsistent and unpredictable," Frank said. "You swing at every pitch, and you are trying so hard that you've gotten into this place where you strike out a lot." Frank pointed to Sam's last four at-bats – four strikeouts on twelve pitches. "Right here, you swung at everything and missed it all."

"I'm terrible," Sam said, slapping his glove on his leg. "I'm just terrible."

"No you aren't," Frank said. "I was terrible. You aren't terrible. Here's what will happen. If you keep saying that, you will become it. You will become terrible, and we don't want that to happen. You are valuable to our team. You are a really good first baseman, and the other boys like being around you. You lift them up. Sam, we need you."

"You ready, Sam?" his dad asked.

"Yes, sir," the boy said, and the three of them took to the field.

⚾ ⚾ ⚾

It was arduous work that Saturday morning. Frank didn't know it, but the two hours he spent with Sam that day were a foreshadowing of the hundreds of hours he would spend with his sons and other boys over more than two decades of coaching.

Frank found a slightly heavier bat in the recreation department's equipment room for Sam to swing. He also told him not to swing at the first fifty pitches. "I just want you to watch them go by and tell me if they are strikes or balls," Frank said. "If they are balls, then you shouldn't swing at them."

"If I don't swing at them, I might walk," Sam asked.

"A walk is just as good as a hit," Frank said. "It's also just dumb to swing at a bad pitch." Frank was pretty sure he could hear Sam's dad laughing from the outfield.

When Frank finally allowed his player to begin swinging, he adjusted Sam's feet in the batter's box and displayed some aggravation when Sam still swung at bad pitches. But throughout their work together, Frank saw a glimmer of hope. Sam watched the pitches that Frank intentionally threw badly, and a few of his hits were dropping over shortstop instead of screaming down the foul line. With each good hit or improved pitch selection, Frank gushed praise on the boy.

At the end of the morning, Sam said, "Coach, can we do this again?"

"When I'm in town on the weekends, we can do this every week," Frank said. "We might even invite one or two other players."

That's just what happened. Frank's father-son workouts even ended with a visit to the nearby McDonald's.

⚾ ⚾ ⚾

Frank let Sam hit without sharing a lineup spot in a 10-6 win over
the Civitan Club. For the first time that season, Sam showed im-
provement. He hit a ball to shortstop and reached base on an error. Sam doubled down the left field line. He grounded out to first,
which caused Frank to look toward heaven and thank the Lord: it
was a ball hit to the right side of the infield.

As Sam walked past Frank, who was coaching first base, he asked,
"Are you upset, Coach?"

"Heaven's no, Sam," Frank said. "You hit the ball to first base!
When you come to bat the first basemen are so bored they've started
eating a sandwich over here. Congratulations!"

Sam grounded out to third base on his next at-bat, but then came
the miracle of miracles. He drew a walk in his last at-bat, and when
he reached first base, Frank offered his hand for Sam to slap.

"Congratulations, my friend," Frank said. "You finally drew a
walk."

Sam rolled his eyes and grinned toward the dugout. His friends
were cheering for him.

Sam was hitless in a win over the Jaycees, and though he struck
out twice, he drew another walk. Facing the undefeated Kiwanis
team in the next game, Sam struck out all three times he came to the
plate. After the game, a 9-3 loss, he was demoralized.

"Maybe next year," he said.

"Sam, that pitcher will probably play high school baseball one
day," Frank said. "Sometimes you just have to tip your hat to the
pitcher and recognize that it was his day to be great – not yours.

Striking out is a part of baseball." He thought Sam wanted to cry. "Did you play well today at first base? Yes you did. Focus on what you do well; the rest will come along."

"I just feel like I'm letting the team down," Sam said.

"Sam, this isn't going to be the worst thing that ever happens in your life," Frank said.

"What will be the worst thing that happens?" he asked.

"Well, lots of things, but the first time you try to kiss a girl and she laughs at you; that will be pretty bad," Frank said, smiling. "That will be worse than striking out on a ball field."

Frank gave a light shove to the boy's shoulder and told him to go home, and the boy smiled and took off at a sprint from the dugout. "See you Saturday!" he shouted.

⚾ ⚾ ⚾

The Lions' next game was against the Mid-Day Optimist Club. Player for player, the Optimists were the Lions' equal, and the two teams were battling for second place behind the Kiwanis Club. In the Stanton league, second place was significant. The league had two summer All-Star teams, and the coaches of the first- and second-place teams often coached those All-Star teams. The coach of an All-Star team could ensure more of his team's players had a chance to play into the summer.

Before the game with the Optimists, Frank told his power-hitting quartet – John, Charles, Jeffrey, and James – that the team would lean heavily on them. Frank dropped Sam to the seven position in the batting order but did not platoon his at-bats with another player.

Frank decided to pitch the Weapon, but the pressure proved to be too great, and that was Frank's fault. He had made too much of this game and its importance to the season. When the Lions came to bat in the top of the third, they were down 6-3.

Jane was coaching third base, and Frank was coaching first with Mack in the dugout. Frank knew Jane was better at running the boys home, while Mack was better as an encourager in the dugout. Frank kept his scorebook, and it was easier to do that in the first base box.

Robbie, the inning's leadoff batter, struck out. John reached on an error at short and then scored when Charles singled. On a hit to the shortstop, Jeffrey reached first on a fielder's choice as Charles was thrown out at second. James walked, putting men at first and second with two outs and the team down 6-4.

As Sam walked to the plate, Frank shouted, "Sam, set your feet the way you want them." He saw the boy's head nod as he stepped into the batter's box.

At that moment, every single thing Frank and Sam had worked on for all of those Saturdays went out the window. In the heat of the moment, Sam didn't do anything he had been coached to do. Frank noticed it right away; Frank noticed that Sam's feet were wide open with his front foot pulled back – a clear sign that he was going to pull the ball out of play – if he was able to reach the ball at all.

On the first pitch, Sam took a mighty swing and missed the ball. Strike one.

The pitcher threw the second pitch; Sam missed it. Strike two.

Sam shook his head. Frank wondered if he was crying.

Mack came to the end of the dugout and said, "Frank, go talk to him. Tell him it's okay."

Frank called time out and motioned Sam toward him.

"Take a big deep breath," Frank told him. "Listen to me. There's no pressure on you. You just pretend like you and me are the only ones out here." He paused. "Well, your dad is out there in left field, but he's not really paying attention."

Sam smiled. "I'm okay, Coach." Frank gave him two pats on the top of the batting helmet. Sam returned to the batter's box beside home plate.

As everyone held their breath, Sam watched the next pitch pass by for a ball.

"Good job," Frank shouted, though he was sure the boy didn't hear him.

Sam cocked like he would swing at the next pitch but held up, and the ball was low. Ball two, and the count was now even at 2-2.

Frank's gut was churning. His team needed to maximize this third inning in a six-inning game, especially with two runners on base.

"Lord, I need this child to get a hit," Frank whispered to himself. "He needs it bad."

The pitcher dug in and threw the next pitch.

Frank dropped into a catcher's squat there in the first base box as Sam pulled the trigger and swung at the pitch. The bat met the ball with an unmistakable sound – aluminum meeting leather – and the ball shot off the bat like it had been launched from a cannon. High and long, toward left center field, it was still climbing when it sailed over the fence for a three-run home run.

Frank threw the scorebook in front of his face as the first base bleachers erupted. His team spilled out of the dugout.

Sam stood and watched it, almost as if it was happening to someone else, and when the home plate umpire shouted, "Home run!" Sam dropped the bat and started in a full run toward first base. When he saw Frank, a smile broke wide on the boy's face. Through misty eyes, Frank was smiling at the boy running in his direction. He kept waiting on Sam to take the turn at first, but he didn't. The boy jumped into Frank's arms, surprising him so badly that the coach and player almost fell back to the ground.

"We did it!" Sam said, and Frank quickly put him down and slapped the top of his batting helmet.

"You did it, and you better touch every base," Frank shouted as the little boy ran toward second with both arms pumping into the sky.

Sam did touch every base, and his entire team was waiting on him at home plate. The Lions went up 7-6 on Sam's three-run homer and battled their way to a 12-10 victory over the Mid-Day Optimists and into second place.

After the game, Frank quietly gave Sam the game ball, which was also the boy's home run ball.

⚾ ⚾ ⚾

Sam finished that season with a .258 batting average. He had more strikeouts than he had hits, but after the home run he never again pulled a ball down the left field line. He made contact to every part of the field. The Lions made the playoffs and made it to the championship game before losing to undefeated Kiwanis in the championship game.

In one playoff game, a 15-6 win over the Civitan Club, Sam led the entire team in hitting, going 3-3 with a single, a walk, a double . . . and another home run – this time a long fly ball to center field.

⚾ ⚾ ⚾

A few weeks after the season, Frank went to his mailbox and pulled out a hand-addressed envelope. On the walk back to his front door, he tore open the envelope and took out a Hallmark card with the picture of a baseball on the front.

"Dear Coach Frank," the note began. "Thank you for coaching my team this year and for helping me with my hitting. I will never forget the home run as long as I live. Your friend, Sam." His mom and dad added their hand-written thanks.

Coach Frank.

At the team's year-end party, complete with trophies and certificates, Jeffrey's dad presented Frank with a team photograph that all the players had signed. In making that presentation, he also referred to Frank as "Coach Frank." During an applause, Frank Wilcox looked around the room, and his eyes settled on a smiling Sam. In that moment, Frank Wilcox knew what it meant to be called a coach.

⚾ ⚾ ⚾

The Braves scored two in the bottom of the third and took a 2-0 lead over the Marlins.

Frank stood up and stretched and then excused himself past Bradley and Whitney. He climbed the steps to the concourse around

Turner Field, and then he turned to look back at the field from this vantage point. There was nothing so sweet as baseball in the spring.

He made his way to the restroom and then stopped by a concession stand for a bag of peanuts. He bought two bags and a bottle of water. Propping against a concrete wall, he smiled at the families out for a game this Wednesday night. Seeing them reminded him of so many outings with his boys to watch the Braves at this very stadium. It always cost him a fortune to bring them, but right now every single memory was worth it.

FOURTH INNING
THE FIELD OF DREAMS

Ding-a-ling-a-ling
Ding-a-ling-a-ling
Pitcher's got an arm like a washing machine
Out of order, Out of order
Need a quarter, Need a quarter

Before walking back down the steps to his seat, Frank paused once more at the top of the aisle. He looked over the field and thought about all the baseball fields he had visited. He thought about the fields on which he had coached.

"Still comes down to a diamond of bases and plenty of room to hit and run," he thought, and smiled.

An usher nudged him from his trance. "You will need to find your seat, sir," she said kindly. "We can't allow people to block this aisle."

"I'm sorry," Frank said. "I was just admiring the field."

She smiled.

"I used to travel a lot, fly all over the country," he said. "As we took off or when we were landing, I looked for baseball fields, and I never failed to find one." He smiled at her and shrugged his shoulders.

"I'm not surprised," she said. "American's Favorite Pastime, right?"

"Yep," he said. "I've even been to the Field of Dreams up in Iowa." He had now moved to the side of the aisle, so he wasn't blocking it. "While I was there, a family showed up, and I threw batting practice to one of the boys while the dad shagged balls in the outfield."

She turned her attention to someone else, clearly a sign that Frank needed to sit down or move out of the aisle. As he walked to his seat, he thought about the Field of Dreams – not the one from the famous movie featuring actor Kevin Costner, but the one at Round Top Baptist Church in Concord, South Carolina.

Richard "Doc" Holladay was tall and athletic, bald-headed, and over-flowing with the gift to encourage others. It just came naturally to him, this giftedness, and he could easily see when a person needed a dose of it. To no one's real surprise, Doc was a funeral director and, he said with a wink and a false sense of propriety, "a cremation specialist." But what he loved was coming alongside a grieving family and genuinely caring for them and encouraging them in the deepest valley of life.

He also loved baseball. He drove an older model blue Ford pick-up that wheezed and huffed every time he cranked it. The funeral home's owners made him park next door at a convenience store, so ashamed were they of his truck and its effect on the polished image of "life's exit doors," as Doc called them. He nicknamed the truck Hearse. He liked to say of his wife Allison, "Miss Allison got the Volvo, but this old Hearse is mine."

Inside the truck's cab was what Doc referred to as his "mobile office," and there were papers scattered everywhere mixed with old dried french fries and empty drink cups with straws sticking from holes in plastic lids. A baseball glove, holding a Wilson baseball, was always on the front seat as if Doc was expecting to drive past a game and jump into a team's lineup.

Everyone who knew Doc had heard the story about him.

He was called out to visit a family whose wife and mother had died. The husband was so grief-stricken that he couldn't even visit the funeral home to make final arrangements. The couple had one child, a nine-year-old boy, and the boy was being smothered by the church's good brethren who descended upon the house with chicken casseroles and baked spaghetti. Doc went to visit the grieving husband, hoping to tie up loose ends around visitation and funeral arrangements.

When Doc pulled down a long, dirt driveway to a small farmhouse, he saw the son sitting on a porch step. Well-wishers walked up and down the steps, occasionally stopping to tell the little boy everything was going to work out well, that God was in control, and that his daddy was surely going to need him more than ever.

Doc got out of the blue truck and took the baseball glove with him. He took off his tie, unbuttoned his top button, and rolled up his white, starched pinpoint Oxford shirt sleeves. He walked up to the little boy.

"Would you like to toss a few?" he asked.

The little boy looked up at him, never said a word, and went for his glove.

He came outside, and Doc said, "Now, one rule. Don't throw it as hard as you can. I still have work to do today, and I can't work if you break my hand." He tossed the ball, and the boy caught it and then tossed it back to him. Back and forth, the ball went, and Doc stepped back some so the boy could throw it a little harder.

"I can tell that you and your daddy have put in some time throwing a baseball," Doc said. "You have great arm action." The throws continued until the boy caught one and slowly crumpled to his knees. The ball dribbled out of his glove. His face fell forward into the ground, and he began sobbing.

"My mama loved to watch me pitch," he said through a gurgled voice that was somewhat silenced by the ground. "*My mama loved me.*"

In just a few steps, Doc was to him, got down on his knees beside him, and pulled the boy to his chest. He held him right there in the yard, and they cried together.

"My mama's gone to heaven too," Doc said. "It's okay to cry it out. Don't let anyone ever tell you differently. My mama saw every game I ever played."

That boy, the one Doc held in that front yard, grew up to lead the Concord High baseball team to a South Carolina state championship, and Doc was there to see every game he pitched. At the end of the season, the boy gave Doc one of the game balls, autographed by the entire team, and Doc kept it under glass on his desk. Doc's wife, Miss Allison, said that baseball meant more to him than anything he owned.

When grieving people asked him about the baseball and its meaning, he simply said, "Baseball is a wonderful salve for the brokenhearted. Nothing makes time stand still like a game of catch."

Doc Holladay was walking out of Round Top Baptist Church the day Frank Wilcox turned into the church parking lot. Doc had been visiting with the church pastor about a funeral service the next day. They were expecting a big crowd, and Doc and the pastor discussed having the service in the church's fellowship hall rather than the sanctuary.

Frank knew of Doc but did not know him well.

Fortunately for that day, and the years forward, Frank lived by one of the several little maxims that he wrote for himself.

"I expect the next person I meet to be the best friend I'll ever have," was one he used in quite a few Baptist Sunday School lessons taught at the big Baptist church on Main Street.

That day at Round Top Baptist Church, that little maxim took on a new life.

⚾ ⚾ ⚾

Before his visit to Round Top Baptist Church – the day he met Doc Holladay for the first time – Frank had been on an arduous six-month dance with the local Concord Dixie Baseball League.

Ten years before, he had left Stanton and moved home to the Atlanta area, taking a job with the daily newspapers in Atlanta. During that time he had helped coach a few teams in a metro Atlanta community. He and Vicki had married, and Frank's newspaper career had moved him to Concord. When they moved, the couple had a toddler and an infant. Now, a handful of years after the move, Frank and Vicki had four sons under the age of eleven. Frank no longer worked in newspaper publishing; he now worked for the South

Carolina Baptists, helping churches across the state make better use of communication strategies within their communities.

Frank and Vicki's oldest son had been playing in the Concord Dixie Baseball League for three seasons already, and Frank had helped a little at practices and agreed to keep the scorebook for the team's head coaches. Now, wrapping up his first season in the Dixie Minor League for nine- and ten-year-olds, the boy's team was without a head coach for the following spring.

Prompted by a friend at church to coach the team, and further tempted to coach his oldest son, Frank was apprehensive. He tried all the familiar excuses: He was too busy, his family was too large, and his job was too consuming. He couldn't give coaching the full-time attention it needed. In the end, a friend whispered in his ear, "Do it out of self-preservation. If you coach, you set the practice schedule around *your schedule*, and you can protect the investment you've made teaching your son how to play the game."

When Frank enrolled his son in that fall's noncompetitive instructional league, casually referred to as "fall ball," Frank inquired about coaching the following spring. He was told there were no guarantees.

A league board member made it known that the league usually had many prospective coaches to choose from and Frank was relatively an unknown – regardless of any past experience in Georgia communities. This was Concord, South Carolina. He could, however, improve his chances of "getting his son's team" if he first agreed to coach fall ball. It would allow Frank to get to know the league and the league to know Frank.

Years later, Frank said, "I was bamboozled. They had no one to coach that spring team, but they needed a fall coach. So they disguised it all as a tryout for the following spring. When I later served as the commissioner of the fall league, I used that little sleight of hand on other dads."

What Frank learned from that alleged tryout season in fall baseball was that it was a unique way to scout players and families coming up from the younger league without the pressure of winning. There was only one practice per week, and games were on Sunday afternoons. The games were more like pickup games, reminding Frank of his youth on the playgrounds of Acorn, Georgia.

Miraculously, after coaching in that season of fall ball, he applied to coach his son's competitive spring team, and his application was excitedly approved. He learned the news one evening when the league commissioner called him.

"Frank," the voice was kind and cautionary, "I want to welcome you to the league. You know we have a pretty big league here. We have more than ninety-six teams, translating into more than 1,100 players, ages five to nineteen. It's quite the organization." There was a long pause – so long that Frank thought the telephone call had been disconnected.

"Hello?" Frank asked.

"Yes, sorry, Frank," the voice said, apologetically. "We don't have enough fields at the ballpark for everyone to practice. Coaches must find their own place to practice." Another pause.

"Where in the world can I find a field?" Frank asked. "I'm not from here. I don't know anyone."

"Well, that's the million-dollar question," the commissioner said. "Good luck."

Good luck, my ass.

After that telephone call, Frank's eyes were opened to the real dilemma at hand – the dilemma he had been sheltered from in his short time around the Concord Dixie Baseball League.

The Concord Dixie League was very competitive in a growing affluent community, and parents wanted their son's team to be competitive. Concord's Dixie League wasn't the pure recreation leagues of Jenson and Stanton, operating under the state-run Georgia Recreation and Parks Society umbrella. Concord baseball was real-deal competitive baseball. The fall ball league was relaxed and fun; the spring league was something altogether different. Fall ball was a nice, fluffy little house cat; spring ball was a raging tiger that had not eaten in a month.

Everyone tried to temper things by saying, "Baseball is just a game," but the truth was that no one in Concord wanted their son to be the neighborhood player on a team that sucked. Parents looked to volunteer coaches to ensure sucking didn't happen. Coaches knew this expectation and knew that sucking was best prevented by lots of practicing, requiring a practice field. Unfortunately, with ninety-six teams fighting and clawing for practice space, practice fields were in high demand. Further complicating this little conundrum was that the league, hoping to avoid angry parents on sucky teams, mandated four to five practices each week alongside one to two games. Baseball coaching was a full-time, volunteer job.

Frank looked at Vicki and said, "I'm starting to understand why no one wants to coach. In Jenson and Stanton, we practiced one or two times each week and had one or two games. No one worried about winning and losing, especially in Stanton. It was all just so low-key. Wow, that's not how it is here." A few years earlier, one of Frank's friends from church had volunteered to coach. When he didn't practice enough, the parents rose and took the team away from the league-appointed coach.

Nothing says competition like a parent-led coup of a nine- and ten-year-old baseball team.

Vicki looked at him and said, "You have to coach. You are good at it." Then she smiled. "We don't want our boys playing on teams that suck." She laughed out loud, and Frank did too, although very nervously.

⚾ ⚾ ⚾

Frank had two weeks to find a practice field. He might as well have searched for hidden Mayan gold in the midlands of South Carolina. Frank called other coaches, called former coaches, and even drove a five-mile radius of Concord, hoping to spot a field as a gift from God. What he learned was that coaches had already staked out the few fields located at church properties. Coaches even joined churches to have access to a field. Some coaches had modified flat pastureland that belonged to the family or close friends, and other coaches had squatted on a vacant lot in or around Concord. Teams practiced anywhere they could find a patch of land.

Frank learned that one coach had stumbled upon an old backstop at the intersection of two country roads. A farmer had put it up a decade before when his daughters were playing recreational softball. The baseball coach begged for the chance to use the old backstop, and the farmer had agreed to the "rental" fee of one hundred dollars per month.

If a coach had once played baseball at Concord High School, there was a chance he could leverage a relationship to use a patch of land at the high school – not on the baseball field, maybe the parking lot – but close enough to say, "We practice at the high school."

Another coach had squatted on the recreation football field and went on to win multiple league championships while all the time practicing on a football field. Teams practiced on daycare center playgrounds, inside church gymnasiums, and on corporate fields normally reserved for employee softball teams. Any patch of land in Concord was a potential practice field – even one player's backyard that was on a twenty-degree slope.

When Frank asked if he could share a patch of land with another coach, there were many unreturned telephone calls and restless shifting of feet. It was a competitive league, and every coach felt the pressure, and sharing a prime field created even more pressure.

One coach confided with Frank over breakfast, "If you share a field and the other team wins a lot and your team does not, well, parents start to turn to the other coach for advice about their boy's hitting or fielding or pitching. Then you've lost control of your team. Did you ever lose a girlfriend to another boy?"

"No," Frank said, pretty assuredly. "That never happened to me."

"Well, believe me, if you practice on the same field with a winning coach, your parents will turn on you faster than you can turn off the lights and jump in bed before the room gets dark." He then looked into Frank's face. "When you lose control of your team, you are done." The way he said *"you are done"* was dark and ominous, and Frank wanted to chuckle over his oatmeal but couldn't.

Finding a field became Frank's challenge and his obsession.

⚾ ⚾ ⚾

As Frank stared out the window, his office telephone rang. Later, he told others that the voice on the other end might as well have been an angel sent directly from the Lord, but it was the new pastor at Round Top Baptist Church located on the outskirts of Concord's city limits. The pastor wasn't calling about baseball – he was calling Frank because his church needed communication counsel, and among South Carolina Baptists, Frank was the one to call.

"I will meet you at the church tomorrow morning," Frank said to the affable pastor. The day was expected to be a beautiful day, and Frank planned to follow up his meeting by driving the area around Concord in search of a field.

⚾ ⚾ ⚾

From Frank's home, Round Top Baptist Church was six miles away.

Even though this part of Concord was close to town, the church's community reminded Frank of his precious childhood along Brookwood Road in Acorn, Georgia. Houses were spread apart, and there was a smaller membership church, no streetlights, and plenty of wide-open space. At night, it was easy to look up and see the stars.

⚾ ⚾ ⚾

As Frank got out of his Ford F-150, he saw Doc Holladay coming out of the church with the pastor. The pastor smiled as Frank walked up and said, "Frank, do you know the esteemed Doc Holladay?"

"I've heard a lot about him," Frank said, shaking the pastor's hand and then extending it to Doc.

"Nice to meet you, Frank," Doc said. "I hope every time I see you that you are upright and breathing."

Frank laughed. "Me too."

Doc turned to the pastor and exchanged a farewell with an encouraging word about the funeral service planned for the next day. Frank quietly looked around the parking lot, waiting on his appointment with the pastor. Frank's gaze went beyond a small clubhouse to a dirt bank behind the church property. Frank guessed the dirt bank rose ten feet tall from its base. From his angle, looking over the crest of that tall dirt bank, Frank thought he saw the tops of several utility poles in the distance.

"Does all that property belong to the church?" he asked, pointing up over the bank.

"It does," the pastor said. "I wish we could do more with that. That is an old ballfield that was built about twenty years ago. The church once had a softball team, and they played games up there."

"Can we walk up there?" Frank asked, trying to hide the excitement in his voice.

"We sure can," the pastor said, and led Frank around behind the church to the narrow dirt road that led from the church parking lot into what would have been left field of the old ballfield. As the field opened up to him, Frank stood there with his mouth wide open. It was the perfect practice field for his team.

"It's Haw Creek," he said to himself.

"What's that?" the pastor asked.

"It reminds me of a field I played on a few times as a boy and then summers when I was in college," Frank said. "The community of Haw Creek had a gigantic field cut out of a pine forest near Haw Creek Baptist Church. My great, great, great grandfather is buried there. You could hit a ball at Haw Creek field and run forever. This field reminds me of Haw Creek."

"Memories are nice, aren't they?" the pastor said, looking out at the old field with its expansive outfield. He pointed to the gap between left and center field and said, "I bet if you hit a ball just right and if you had the speed, you could clear the bases."

Neither of them noticed that Doc Holladay had walked up to the field with them.

"I'd say you got a regular Field of Dreams here, pastor," Doc said. "You might dream of it being used as ballfield one day." Frank didn't hear him. He was too busy soaking up the field in front of him. Weeds were growing in the infield, and he could tell the bases were in really poor shape. Old wire, used to build chicken pens, was strung between those utility poles, creating a backstop. Unsupported and stretched over time, the wire sagged. The outfield – truly a field – was wonderfully flat, dormant and brown right now, but Frank imagined it came alive with green weeds during the hot spring and summer. As Frank looked closer, past first base, he could see an old bench, which would have been used by the home team. Beyond that, it looked like there was a pitcher's mound – probably someone's makeshift bullpen.

It was beautiful. Frank wanted to cry. He actually wanted to drop to his knees and thank the Good Lord Almighty, but decorum prevented it. He was also not a Pentecostal.

"Pastor," Frank started and paused, "do you think I could use this field? I've signed on to coach baseball, nine- and ten-year-olds, and we desperately need a place to practice."

"I don't see why not," the pastor said. "There's a spirit in this church to let the community use its facilities. That's just one of the reasons I love the people here. They approach the world with their hands wide open to give away. I'll get you the name of the chairman of our facilities committee; he is the one you need to speak with."

Frank wanted to hug the pastor right there, squeeze the guts right out of him, and promise to send him birthday presents and Christmas cards.

"Say, Frank," Doc said. "You want to toss a few? I got my glove in the truck."

"I would love to, more than anything, really, but I came out to meet about this church's communication system," Frank said.

The pastor, as genteel a man as God ever created, knew he was beaten and smiled.

"You men take some time and just be boys again," he said. "Frank, come on to the office when you are finished. I've got some telephone calls to make regarding the funeral service tomorrow."

In minutes, Frank Wilcox had produced a Nokona catcher's mitt and returned to Doc Holladay, waiting in the scrub-grassed, mostly dirt left field. The two men rolled up their sleeves and loosened ties and started throwing.

"Looks like you could put in some time on this old field, and it will work just fine for practices," Doc said. "These are really good people; that pastor is first-class all the way."

Frank caught a throw and returned it. "I've coached before, but this will be my first time in Concord. Folks here take their baseball a lot more seriously than I've experienced elsewhere. I'm nervous and excited all at the same time."

"You got someone helping you?" Doc asked him. "I've never coached, but if it's as competitive as you seem to think, you are going to need help."

"I hope I get a player or two with dads interested in helping," Frank said, returning another volley.

Doc held the ball and stared at Frank, sizing him up.

"I'll help you, Frank," he said. "Well, if you need me, that is. You might find it easier if you've got an assistant coach who isn't someone's dad. Dads can surely help and should if they are interested. But you might like having a coach who isn't tied up in dinner conversations about his son's playing time and position."

Frank liked this man. He was honest and straightforward, but he was well-spoken and thoughtful.

"Have you always had that nickname, Doc?" Frank asked, catching the delayed throw.

"Yep," he said. "My daddy loved western movies, and he thought it was funny. I suspect most people around Concord don't even know my first name is Richard. They just call the funeral home and ask for Doc. Of course, it comes with its share of tired old jokes. I could decorate a room with gifts I've received regarding the OK Corral."

"You ever been to the OK Corral?" Frank asked, and Doc said he had not. "I've been there twice, and it's pretty interesting, but not nearly as glamorous as you think it might be."

The two men threw a few more pitches together, and Frank said, "I need to get inside and see the pastor. But, yes, I'd love to have your help with this team . . . and this field."

Doc laughed out loud. "I suppose you'll need more help with the field than the team, but I'll do all I can to help you." The two men shook hands, and Doc gave Frank all of his contact information.

⚾ ⚾ ⚾

When Round Top Baptist Church was built, the church's front lawns sloped down to the road. Contractors cleared the property up the hill behind the church and moved the dirt down to create the church's front yard.

Clearing the back property allowed the church to plant outfield grass, put up the utility poles, and string wire as a rudimentary backstop. Bases were installed, and for years the church had adult teams that played church-league softball. The field also became a part of the church's fellowship ministry and was used for Vacation Bible School and summer picnic activities.

As a cycle of families grew up in the church and moved away, the field was used less and less. The outfield grass crept into the infield. The old wire backstop rusted and came unhinged from the utility poles. The bases disappeared, and home plate seemed to sink into the soft sand of the infield. When Frank Wilcox discovered the field, it was still in fine shape for a practice field, but it had long been abandoned as a serious field for organized play.

The chairman of the facilities committee was happy for Frank to use the field and was even happier when Frank volunteered to treat it as his own. Frank promised to cut the outfield grass, repair the infield, and, as best he could, reattach wire to the poles. The church was happy that the air around the old field would be filled with children's voices and the property would be reclaimed. It was a win for Frank and a win for the church.

"I just need you to be flexible if we have a funeral or a wedding," the pastor said. "It would probably be best if you didn't practice or

play when big church events are happening." Frank completely understood that request – though there was a day in future years when
a scrimmage and a funeral occurred on the same preseason Saturday.

Frank felt so bad about the communication mix-up that he waited a week before calling the deceased man's widow and apologizing
for the noise that might have leaked into the funeral proceedings.

"Honey," the woman on the other end said, "my husband loved
children, and he loved baseball. You didn't disturb us one bit, and
I know John loved that children were playing ball right outside his
funeral service. In heaven, I bet he was watching your game instead
of the service."

⚾ ⚾ ⚾

Frank and Doc went to work on the field, meeting each evening for
an hour and then on Saturday mornings. They cut the weeds in the
outfield. They used a tiller to turn over the infield. A makeshift field
drag was tied to Frank's pickup hitch, and the infield was leveled.
Doc built up the pitcher's mound while Frank measured out and
installed brand new rubber bases. With extension ladders, they reat-
tached the chicken wire behind home plate.

Frank used a Weed Eater to clean up the area around first base,
and the two men built a place for pitchers to work during practice.
Doc discovered an old metal hitting tee that been tossed into the
adjacent pine woods. Using a lubricant, he was able to clean the tee
to adjust to different heights. A friend who was tearing down an old
batting cage gave Frank some of the netting. Doc used it to build a
hitting station where boys could hit off the tee into a net.

The men were working so hard one Saturday morning that they failed to notice the guest who had walked into the infield and now stared stone-faced at them. Her name was Roxie. Roxie was a black-and-tan rottweiler.

⚾ ⚾ ⚾

"Oh crap," Frank whispered, and tapped Doc on the shoulder. "Don't make any sudden moves."

Doc turned to see what had caught Frank's attention and took a startled step backward. Standing in the middle of the infield, staring at them, was the rottweiler. She didn't bark. She just stared, curiously wondering what these two men were doing.

"Let's just keep working and see what she does," Doc said.

"I'm not so sure I want to wait around," Frank said, laughing nervously. "What if she does something that requires about a hundred stitches."

"If she meant to hurt us, she would," Doc said. "She would probably be barking."

The two men continued raking and leveling dirt around the first base practice area when Doc poked Frank in the side with the rake's end. Frank turned to look at the large dog, and she was lying down in the sun-soaked infield. She panted as she watched the men, and Frank thought she could have been smiling.

A voice pierced the air, "Roxie! Roxie! Come here, girl."

The rottweiler stood and looked toward a nice brick home hidden behind a thin layer of woods along the third baseline. She ambled toward the voice coming from a slender man sporting a black mustache and wearing jeans with a plaid shirt. Frank guessed him to be about the age of his dad.

"Looks like you are getting the old field in fine shape," he said from the edge of the woods. "We go to the church down there." He pointed to the church. "I'm glad you all can use this field again. My name's Dale, and my wife is Mary, and we're here if you need us for anything."

"That's a pretty rottweiler," Doc said.

"This is Roxie," Dale said. "She won't bother anyone. She might walk down here to see what you are doing from time to time, but she's as gentle as they come. She just looks scary, and that's okay." He turned back toward his house, and Roxie followed him through the thin woods and back to the house.

Frank and Doc sat down on a picnic table that Frank had relocated from his house to the field. Over the next two decades, the picnic table would be the site of many team meetings and a serving station for team picnics.

"We don't have a bathroom, Frank," Doc said. "I guarantee you we are going to need a bathroom. You think the team can use one down at the church building?"

Frank laughed. "Doc," he said, holding up two hands toward the thick pine woods behind the first baseline. "We have the largest bathroom in Concord. If someone has to pee, we just send them to the woods."

"You're right," he said. "I will make sure I have toilet paper and hand cleaner in my truck for the other."

"Or leaves and dirt," Frank said, laughing.

The hard work on the Field of Dreams was completed two days before the first practice. The field became a special place for Frank

Wilcox for many years. He often cut the outfield grass with a push mower and used the time to pray over job possibilities, friends and family, and the baseball season ahead. On those days, he felt alone there with God.

And with Roxie, who always came to rest in the sun or shade and visit.

⚾ ⚾ ⚾

Frank's first player draft in the Concord Dixie League was on Valentine's Day – a Sunday afternoon – in the league's board room. The board room was a one-room hut with four 8-foot tables completing a square. Stacks of old equipment circled the walls, and chairs of varying heights and sizes lined the table. There was even an old recliner that no longer reclined and might have been pissed on by a wandering cat. The twenty coaches sat in the order of their draft pick.

The day before, each of the coaches had gathered at the field for the annual player assessment. It was a time for coaches to see the rising talent and assess players' ability to hit, throw, catch, and run. Though Frank had not coached in Concord, he had lived here for several years and knew many of the boys and their families. He also benefitted from having coached the previous fall in the league's noncompetitive instructional league, which introduced him to even more talent.

The night before the draft, he camped out with his oldest son at a Cub Scout Jamboree and tossed and turned all night anticipating the draft. There were ten boys he wanted, and if somehow he could get two of them, it would be a small victory.

He got one of those ten – his first pick. He was amazed at how hard many of the coaches had studied players, talked among themselves, talked with families, and scored the players at assessment. He also learned that some nefarious families told their sons to throw the assessment and do poorly so other coaches would avoid them and leave them open for the coach of their choice. Frank got an education during that first draft. It was high stakes.

When he walked out of that draft, his mind was spinning. It went well enough. By drawing a new team sponsor, Frank was assigned the owner's son, who, as it turned out, was a great ballplayer who could play the catcher's position. Frank also picked up a very athletic older player to join his two returning pitchers, nicknamed Big A and Elvis, and several others he knew were great ballplayers and athletes from the younger league.

He called Doc when he got home and delayed his new friend's Valentine's date with Miss Allison.

"I think we're ready, Doc," Frank said.

"Welp," Doc said, "ready or not, here we come. Let's play ball."

⚾ ⚾ ⚾

That first afternoon of practice, one month from opening day, Frank parked his Ford behind the backstop on the third baseline. He parked there several hundred times over the next two decades. He and Doc sat on the tailgate of his pickup. Roxie ambled down from the house and sat just at the edge of the woods. She never barked once.

They started arriving – parents driving up the small road into left field and then parking along the grass line's edge at the big dirt bank. Boys poured out of cars, pickup trucks, and over-sized sport utility vehicles. Parents – mostly moms – walked their boys up to the coaches they hadn't officially met.

The biggest boy on the team, a towering, outgoing and friendly boy, Big G, approached the coaches and said, "Hey, Coach, is this going to be our field for every practice?"

Reminded of how the field had looked weeks before, Doc Holladay smiled at how much better it looked now. It was a testimony to the hard work he and Frank had invested over the past few weeks.

Doc proudly smiled and said, "Yes, this is our practice field. Welcome to the Field of Dreams."

Big A, who would lead the team in pitching and hitting that year, spread his arms wide and echoed Doc by saying, "The Field of Dreams!"

Picking up a baseball for warm-ups, a chubby kid wearing a Superman T-shirt said under his breath, "Well, I think it looks like crap." Frank could not help but smile as he made the boy run four laps around the entire field.

"Don't ever talk bad about my little answered prayer!" he shouted behind his dark sunglasses. "I'll run you until you puke." He laughed to himself and then noticed a wide-eyed little boy staring at him. "I'm just kidding. I don't want him to puke." Frank smiled at him and patted the top of his cap.

Frank's first team in Concord, with all its youth, finished 9-8 on the season.

Frank squeezed by Bradley and Whitney to retake his seat next to Phil and the boys. Vicki would laugh at him for buying a seat that wasn't on the aisle because Frank Wilcox – *her Frank Wilcox* – always sat on the aisle, whether it was at church, at the movie theatre, on airplanes, or at concerts. Frank rolled his eyes at the thought of her gasping in disbelief.

"You didn't miss anything," Phil said. "Pretty boring game."

Frank smiled. Watching baseball wasn't boring; watching baseball required patience, knowing something big was coming. If that something big didn't come, well, maybe it would the next game.

The woman behind Frank said, "Nothing beats a nice night at the ballpark." Frank turned to smile at her and noticed she had needles and thread in her lap, obviously working on a cross-stitch project.

"Looks like you came prepared," he said.

"Dear, I'm always prepared," she said. "I've had to sit through so many baseball games, watching my two boys. I always come out with a few distractions."

In the fourth, the Braves and Marlins went scoreless. The Braves led 2-0.

FIFTH INNING
THE ROSEWOOD RAINSTORM

Down by the river
Took a little walk
Met up with the other team
Had a little talk
Threw 'em in the river
Hung 'em up to dry
We can beat the other team
Any old time

Frank felt a raindrop and then a few others as a sprinkle began. A spindly index finger tapped him on the collar bone, and he turned his head to the right without fully looking around. The woman's voice behind him said, "It's rain you are feeling – we didn't spill beer on you. I promise." She laughed, and Frank laughed with her. She had already stuffed her cross-stitch into a large bag and placed it under her seat.

The man behind him now also leaned down. "Just a passing little shower – weatherman says about a ten-minute sprinkle." In front of Frank, the little boys turned their faces directly to the sky and opened their mouths, seeing if they could catch a raindrop or five in their open mouths. More rain hit their faces than fell into their mouths.

Frank noticed that the Braves' grounds crew was on standby along the first base wall, but as of yet, had not moved to unroll the tarp. It was just a springtime sprinkle and nothing more, and no one seemed particularly worried that it would become a steady downpour.

The little boys continued to catch drops in their mouths, and the older man with them reached up to tweak the nose of one boy. "You boys look like hungry little birds," he said. Just on cue, the boys began making chirping sounds and flapping their arms like wings.

"Sit down, boys," the younger man said. "Goofy and rain don't mix."

"Truer words were never spoken," Frank thought to himself. Frank wrote "Rosewood" at the top of the scorebook. "Goofy and rain surely don't mix."

⚾ ⚾ ⚾

Doc Holladay stuck his fingers through the wire mesh fencing and looked out at the baseball field. It was raining hard – so hard that the wind blew an occasional spray through the dugout. The spray was a reprieve from the early July heat and humidity, but Doc seemed worried about the pools of water forming in the coaching boxes by first and third base. Besides, the rainy spray into the old, dirty, sweaty dugout made everything smell like a wet dog.

Frank eased up beside him.

"What do you think, Doc?" Frank said. "Think we'll have to come back tomorrow and finish?"

"Looks like it's draining pretty well, and the sky might be clearing back over there," he said, nodding his head toward the west. The city's rain almost always came from the west, and Frank did see a break in the evening clouds.

"Supposing we get to finish it," Frank paused midsentence. "You think we can win it?"

Doc never looked away from the field.

"Yes, sir," he said. "Throw the Big Train out there and let that engine roll." Frank noticed his gaze turn toward third base and the opponent's dugout. "Look at those fools over there."

Frank stared beyond the rain. The opposition's dugout was empty, and the entire team was playing in the rainstorm. Several of the boys were running and sliding along on rain-soaked grass. Frank turned and looked at his team. They sat serious-faced on the dugout bench. Not even the wind's wet gusting affected them.

"Their coach over there is a McClain," Doc said. "I embalmed his grandmama. The family gene pool ended when that sainted woman entered heaven." Frank laughed without opening his mouth.

"You are too much," Frank said.

"Me?" Doc slapped a hand on his chest in shock. "I believe you just threw a poor mama out of our dugout because she brought her son a hot dog. That was cold."

Frank continued laughing. "There's no eating in the dugout."

"Lord, look at her, Coach Frank," Doc said, nodding his head toward the team's bleachers, where the mom sat huddled with others underneath big umbrellas. "She had to eat that wiener herself and pout all at the same time. She's still pouting."

"I probably shouldn't have yelled at her in front of everyone," Frank said.

139

"You should apologize after the game," Doc said, winking. "Or not. Either way, I'm going to make fun of you for a long time."

"I do not doubt that," Frank said.

Frank could not wait for the rain to end. He was ready to get this game finished.

⚾ ⚾ ⚾

It was a twisting road that led Frank and Doc to Columbia, South Carolina's Rosewood Field for that summer's All-Star tournament. Every Concord All-Star team's journey began at the Concord ballpark.

Rumored to be forty years old, the ballpark was in ill repair, but a glorious place for families and friends to gather each spring and summer. There was nothing pristine about the old park, which meant no one got upset if a window was accidentally broken or someone's little sister drew flowers on a broken sidewalk with colored chalk. If a T-baller couldn't hold his bladder to make the bathroom, no one cared if his parents let him pee between cars in the parking lot. Everyone knew just about everyone, and knew their children, and looked after one another's children. The Concord Dixie Baseball community was family, and opening day every March was like a giant family reunion – though a fried bologna sandwich from the concession stand replaced Aunt Dolly's banana pudding. Opening day also meant picture day because all the uniforms were clean, and a kind photographer and his beautiful wife spent all day taking team and individual photographs while encouraging players and joking with coaches.

The park featured two twin fields, one for nine- and ten-year-olds, and a second for eleven- and twelve-year-olds. The dimensions were the same, which meant the eleven- and twelve-year-old boys had a home run possibility at every at-bat. To make the long ball more challenging, the outfield fence was raised ten feet, creating an arena-ball effect. It was possible to hit a long single off the left field fence and then have it carom all the way to right field, giving the hitter a triple. Anything could happen on that field. But on the adjacent nine- and ten-year-old field, the game was more like baseball as God intended.

There was a pony field for the thirteen- and fourteen-year-olds. The youngest boys, the T-ballers, had their own field just beyond left field of the Pony League field. When a Pony Leaguer hit a foul ball or a long home run, everyone shouted, "Heads up!" or "Incoming!" because balls dropped like bombs on the crowd, and many a car in a small parking lot within the ballpark had windows busted. It was rumored that a long home run landed in the middle of a T-ball game, and the little ones began chasing the ball – never understanding or caring how it dropped from the sky.

The oldest players played in the Colt League, which was reserved for fifteen- to nineteen-year-olds, and the Colt League field was a regulation high school field. It was unusual, but not out of the question, for one of the oldest boys in Colt League to show up for a game with his wife – maybe even a baby. One shortstop called time out to smoke a cigarette because he was nervous during a championship game.

There was an old worn-out football field in the center of all the baseball action. A horse track, reserved for show horses, was down in the bottoms of the ballpark near an old softball field affectionately called "Field Nine." That dark corner of the ballpark was the perfect dark place for teenagers to make out in the dew of the outfield.

Each of the fields had a two-story cinder-block structure used for operating the scoreboard, and home teams had to provide a scoreboard operator. The bottom of the structures was used for equipment storage.

In the center of the complex was an old equipment shed packed with US Army duffle bags, presumably from nearby Fort Jackson, that were now used as equipment bags for head coaches to borrow. Beside the equipment shed were two long batting cages, though the caging was rotten fabric that allowed baseballs to fly all the way down to the Colt League field. After a full week of use, the sand-and-dirt floor of the cages was dug out on either side of two home plates, so that on Saturday the batters were actually standing ankle-deep in holes.

The centerpiece of the entire complex was a cinder-block concession stand – "the canteen" – with a covered waiting area that provided just about the only shelter from electrical storms. When a storm came up, everyone got really cozy under the concession stand's waiting area. Nothing said family like the pressed-together mixture of boyhood sweat, active men's deodorant, and Victoria's Secret perfume worn by a few of the manhunters.

The men's and women's bathrooms opened to that sheltered area. The women's bathroom was nasty by the end of a long Saturday – though nary a woman dared sit completely down on the toilet seat; the men's bathroom, used by all the men and boys at the ballpark, was like a latrine, and in the hot summer months, well, typhoid shots might have been necessary.

The canteen itself had everything needed for a day at the ballpark. Different colors of Powerade, known by the color instead of the flavor; sunflower seeds; candy; hot dogs and hamburgers; fried bologna sandwiches; french fries; and four-piece chicken baskets. You could even get a BBQ sandwich, which came frozen but microwaved nicely. What's more, parents worked the concession stand, and many a mama slipped a sweet little player a free drink and candy bar. It was hard to say no to sweet little faces that walked up with no money and outstretched hands. If the manager of the concession knew your "mama and them," you could run credit at the concession stand, and many a butt got chewed for running up a tab on Cow Tales, Blow Pops, Big League Chew, and Ring Pops.

In the cold early months of the season, it was not unusual for a coach or two to rush into the canteen to get warm, even warming hands over the deep fryer. The canteen was also home for all things first aid, including ice for when a batter got pegged by an opposing pitcher. When a player got pegged, the fans shouted, "Shake it off, we got ice!" That was someone's cue to run to the canteen for a bag of ice.

On an exterior canteen wall, the one closest to the playground that had to be netted as protection from the Pony League's foul balls, a game of wall ball began before the first game of the day and continued all day long with players coming and going as they had time to play. Wall ball was a made-up game, involving a tennis ball, with closely-held rules, and parents were not privileged to those rules. No adult at the ballpark fully understood how wall ball was played. The ground was chewed up into a dirt and sand mosh pit from the rubber baseball cleats worn by the players.

Near the concession stand, between the pony field for thirteen- to fourteen-year-olds and the minor league field for nine-to-ten-year-olds, was the square board room, where board meetings were held once per month, and coaches gathered for regular meetings, including the league-specific drafts each February. It and the canteen were the only air-conditioned spots in the entire ballpark.

The ballpark was beautiful and wonderful and glorious, and there was no fanfare when it was ultimately torn down for a progressive new ballpark built for big tournaments and travel baseball. As bulldozers and loaders tore down the old ballpark, many a boy – many a coach – cried over the loss of a community icon and all the memories made there.

⚾ ⚾ ⚾

Frank's journey that season, from the Concord ballpark to the All-Star tournament at Rosewood, began in February when Frank assembled that year's version of the Sharks. Frank felt good about the season ahead. He returned seven players, three or four of whom he predicted to be All-Stars from the division's six-team field. Frank picked up another five in the draft and expected three of them to compete with older boys for infield positions. He had pitching, he had two catchers, and he had team speed.

What Frank didn't have was offense. Believing in pitching and defense, Frank was prepared for what he got offensively, and what he got that season was streaky contact hitting.

"I swear, Doc, I can predict by the day of the week whether they hit or not," Frank lamented after one game. "And any game we play on Saturday before eleven or after two, forget it. We may only win 1-0."

"Still a win, Coach," Doc said. "Still a win."

The Sharks' primary competition that season was a team not unlike his own the year before – young and aggressive. The Bears were built on younger, gifted players with a small collection of older players who provided strength at key places on the field and in the lineup. A former pitcher on a Concord High state championship team led the Bears. Between him and his dad, an assistant coach, the pair had forgotten more about baseball than Frank would ever know, and Frank knew it.

The first time the two teams met, the Sharks jumped to a 5-0 lead in the first inning and then sleepily squandered it and lost 8-7. The game ended on a bang-bang double play at third. When the teams met again, the Sharks won 13-7.

As the season's calendar turned from April's pleasant days to the broiling heat of May, the Sharks and their unpredictable hitting began to wilt. Frank was beside himself. Against considerably weaker rosters, the team had eked out wins of 4-2 and 2-1 before losing to the Bears, 5-1, for the second time of the season.

Stalking to the parking lot, Frank threw the equipment bag in the back of his Ford pickup. He turned to glare at Doc, who was coming up behind him. "Don't start with that encouragement crap, Doc. I don't want to hear it. I'm hot and tired, and I'm frustrated."

"Well, you did a good job hiding it from the boys," Doc sarcastically said. "But as I overheard it, they expect Monday's practice to be brutal. One of your outfielders said he was going to ask his mama to make a dentist appointment."

Frank didn't smile. "I'll be calmed down by Monday."

Doc pushed his cap back on his head. "Coach, we just can't hit. It's the reality."

"It makes me sick," Frank said. "We practice five times a week, and hit, hit, hit. I don't understand it. Maybe we practice too much. I don't know."

He got in his truck and left Doc standing in the parking lot.

⚾ ⚾ ⚾

Frank tossed and turned the night after losing to the Bears. Preseason, the Sharks were expected to win the division pretty handily. He had thought so too. Now the team was in a dogfight for the division title; Frank knew the ballpark's old hands were whispering about his ability to win.

"They are saying you might be in over your head," another coach harshly told him one Saturday at the ballpark. "They say Frank Wilcox can't win."

"Who is saying that?" Frank asked.

The coach shrugged his shoulders. The "they" were some of Frank's team's parents.

Frank tossed and turned so much that night that Vicki finally rolled over and said, "Get out of the bed until you are ready to sleep. I can't take all this moving around."

Aggravated, Frank got out of the bed and stalked into the family room, where he sat in a brown recliner, in the pitch dark of the room, and sulked. The house was quiet.

In that contemplative silence, Frank heard something. Well, maybe he didn't audibly hear something, but he remembered something. Frank remembered back years before, standing alongside that fence in Jenson. He remembered the words of Terry Thompson.

"It's not about baseball; it's about the boys."

Frank sighed heavily and drifted off to sleep, finishing the night in the recliner.

⚾ ⚾ ⚾

At Monday's practice, Frank called his team around the tailgate of his pickup.

"I want to apologize to you, boys," Frank said. "I've gotten so caught up in winning this division that I've forgotten that we're playing a game out here." The boys stared at him – even the one who regularly drew in the dirt.

Frank reached back into the bed of the truck and pulled forward a portable stereo, which most everyone referred to as a boombox.

"Are we going to listen to music?" Hammer, the team's first baseman, asked him.

"Yes," Frank said. "Boys, I'm going to introduce you to KC & the Sunshine Band."

⚾ ⚾ ⚾

On Sunday, after losing on Saturday to the Bears and sleeping in the recliner, Frank noticed his sons huddled around the television watching VHS tapes of the Walt Disney Company's film franchise, *The Mighty Ducks*. The movies were about a kids hockey team, in various versions, and against different odds, overcoming the odds to succeed.

Sitting with his boys, Frank began to notice that as the hockey team rallied for its final push to success, the film's rally sequences were to music. He watched as his boys seemed drawn to those scenes much as he had as a high school student watching Rocky Balboa training for a heavyweight fight in the first of the Rocky motion pictures. Frank wondered if he could use music to calm his boys during batting practice, and perhaps ignite them simultaneously.

The next day – Monday – he left work early and purchased a KC & the Sunshine Band Greatest Hits compact disc. KC & the Sunshine Band, a disco and funk band, formed in 1973 in South Florida. The band's music had been popular when Frank was in high school and college. Preparing for practice, Frank took the boombox and the CD to the Field of Dreams for his great experiment.

⚾ ⚾ ⚾

With the boombox on the ground just behind him on the Field of Dreams' makeshift pitcher's mound, Frank threw batting practice that Monday to KC & the Sunshine Band's greatest hits. The practice was immediately looser – more like a party – and the boys started pounding the baseball.

At one point, Frank looked to his outfield, and the three boys were noticeably dancing in place even if they didn't realize it.

After that practice, Big G asked, "Coach, are we going to do this at every practice?"

Before Frank could answer, Doc said, "We are never going to stop doing this." Doc patted Frank on the shoulder and dropped his sunglasses over the bridge of his nose. "Let's boogie."

"Boogie?" someone asked.

"Ask your mom and dad," Frank said.

At pregame batting practice, before the very next game, Frank had the players meet him at the ballpark's batting cages a full seventy-five minutes before game time. He met them with the team's equipment bag slung over one shoulder. He carried the boombox. Frank stepped into the old, decaying batting cages and placed the boombox behind him. The team saw it too. Before the music even began, some of them were dancing in place. The music had cranked their motors.

"We are going to hit in the order you will hit during the game," Frank said. "Everyone get ready to take ten swings, and we will go through the lineup twice. Don't make me wait on you." He took a bucket of baseballs into the batting cage and got behind an L-screen for protection. Then he cranked up the stereo.

That's how the Sharks finished the season: taking public batting practice to KC & the Sunshine Band's dance tunes. It paid off. The very next game, the team won 5-3 and then won again 13-4. In the last game of the season, Adam, a pitcher–shortstop, singled in extra innings to score Matthew for the victory. That win forced a one-game playoff with the Bears, which the Sharks won 6-3, and with it the season's division championship. The team finished the season with a 17-5 record.

Frank was tapped to coach the division's All-Star team, representing Concord.

Working with the other division coaches to build the All-Star team was not difficult. Frank took six of his players and added another seven from the remaining five teams. In the end, every position was strengthened, pitching was added, and hitting improved. Frank enlisted the Bears head coach to assist he and Doc, and that move further strengthened the team.

Within South Carolina Dixie Youth Baseball, local All-Star teams worked their way through a series of local, regional, and state tournaments toward a goal of playing in the Dixie Baseball World Series reserved for state championship teams. Losing in just one of the preliminary double-elimination tournaments ended a team's season.

The first of the qualifying tournaments was at the Rosewood Field in Columbia's downtown district. In the opener, the All-Stars won big, 17-3, and Frank saved two of his best pitchers for tougher competition.

Frank's boys won a thriller in game two, 4-3, but not without a little mid-inning drama in the third. Frank started one of his most reliable pitchers, Rodney, who went by Slim, a boy who didn't walk very many hitters. Most of Frank's pitchers were known for control because he didn't mind balls being put in play when he built his defensive teams.

In this game, however, Slim was anything but reliable. Frank was concerned when he watched his reliable pitcher walk two batters that allowed the opponent from Northeast to go up 3-1. Frank could hear worrisome parents talking behind him, offering advice to him through loud conversations with one another.

"This hot dog sure is good," one dad said loudly. "I wonder if Coach Frank knows he's got another pitcher?"

"My boy could be out there helping," another dad responded. "How old do you figure this ballpark to be?"

"Something's wrong with Slim," Doc whispered to Frank. "Go calm him down, Coach."

Frank called a time out and approached the mound. His pitcher was fighting back the tears.

"What in the world is wrong with you?" Frank asked, putting a hand on the boy's shoulder. He had never seen this kind of emotion from Slim.

"Coach, I have to go to the bathroom."

"You can't hold it for one more out?"

"No, sir," the boy said. "I have to poop."

"Well, when you gotta go, you gotta go," Frank said, taking the boy's glove and pointing to the bathroom just past the right-field fence. "Hurry."

As Slim ran for the outfield fence, the plate umpire jerked off his mask and quickly walked out to the pitcher's mound. He was joined by the visiting team's third base coach and the infield umpire.

"What's going on, coach? Your player can't just run off the field," the umpire said. "You have to bring in another pitcher."

Frank whispered, "Look, he had to poop."

"Poop?" the opposing coach asked, spitting sunflower seeds into a plastic bottle. It was a disgusting habit, and Frank hated seeing it.

"Whatever *you* call it," Frank said, "It's similar to *you* spitting in that bottle. He had to go, and I was afraid he would have an accident out here on the mound."

"Is he sick?" the opposing coach asked, now hiding the plastic bottle behind his back and wiping his mouth with his shirt sleeve.

"I don't know," Frank said. "I think we should treat this as an injury. Let's ask him if he can continue when he gets back."

"An injury?" the umpire asked.

"What else are you gonna call it?" Frank asked.

Slim's dad was now at the fence beside the dugout. Frank held up his hand and said, "He's okay."

Frank called his second baseman, Sugarman, over to the mound. "Go check on Slim."

The boy took off for the bathroom and disappeared inside.

In minutes, the pitcher came running back toward the field, but Sugarman did not.

"Son, are you sick?" the umpire asked him.

"No, sir, I was about to have an accident," the boy said, now sheepishly smiling, taking his glove from Frank.

"Where's Sugarman?" Frank said, and then looked up to see his second baseman running out of the bathroom.

As Sugarman returned to his position, he shouted toward the mound for all to hear, "Sorry, Coach, I had to pee." He turned to his best friend, Hammer, who was at first base and said, "I figured I was already in there."

The umpire looked at Frank. "Anybody else need a third-inning bathroom break?"

The visiting coach looked at the umpire and asked, "Can these boys continue after leaving the field?"

"Yes, and not another word of it," the home plate umpire said, turning and walking back in that direction. "Coach, have your boys do their business between innings. Let's play ball."

Frank was smiling as he returned to the dugout and saw Slim's dad standing there.

"Was he sick?"

"No," Frank said. "Nature called. It happens to the best of us."

With intestinal relief, Slim struck out the next batter swinging and ended the inning. He scored what became the winning run in the bottom of the fourth inning and finished the game with two of the team's runs batted in.

There was a dugout conversation among the boys that the bathroom was without toilet paper, and Frank was afraid to investigate or ask questions. He just accepted the win and did not shake Slim's hand after the game.

In the third game of the tournament, the All-Stars blew a 6-0 lead in the second inning and lost 9-7. It was a collapse, and everyone behind Frank's team knew their coach had misplayed his pitching and stayed with his middle reliever too long. In the fourth game, battling back from the loser's bracket, Frank stuck with his starter for four innings and walked away with a 12-1 mercy win. That win set up a one-game, winner-takes-all championship game on a night scheduled to include a South Carolina summer thunderstorm.

Knowing it was a winner-take-all to advance to the second-round tournament the following week, Frank had no trouble choosing the game's pitcher. Aaron, a tall, quiet, rangy, athletic kid, had been the best pitcher on his regular season's team, if not the entire division. Frank had nicknamed him "Big Train" after the early twentieth-century's power pitcher Walter Perry "Big Train" Johnson. For fifty-six years, long after his death, Johnson had been Major League

Baseball's all-time strikeout king and still ranked as the leader in career shutouts.

So happy to have Big Train on the All-Star team, Frank found a large wooden whistle at a Cracker Barrel restaurant's gift shop. The whistle sounded just like a freight train when it was blown. Frank had the whistle in the dugout and blew it every time Aaron took the mound.

The championship game was against Eastonola, which had given the All-Stars their only loss in this small tournament. While Frank was confident his boys could win behind its Big Train, he also knew Eastonola was throwing its best power pitcher as well. There was no tomorrow.

On an infield error followed by a triple, Eastonola jumped to a 1-0 lead in the first inning.

In the top of the second, Big Train struck out three of the four hitters that he faced. That same inning, the Concord All-Stars came back with singles by Daryl and Mark. Mark had been Frank's catcher during the regular season. When Calvin, the team's leadoff hitter, reached on a fielder's choice, Mark scored from third base, tying the game.

In the top of the third, Eastonola scored off a rare error at third base, and then went up 3-1 in the fifth on three straight singles. The Concord All-Stars could get nothing going on offense and were now down to their last six outs of the game.

That's when the rains came. The flash of lightning, the boom of thunder, and the skies opened up. Someone yelled out, "Everyone get in their cars!" which Frank always thought sounded like "Head for the hills!" as a euphemism for avoiding a natural disaster or bootleggers running from Treasury agents.

"No," Frank said matter-of-factly as some of his team started to leave the dugout. "We are going to sit on this dugout bench and wait it out."

"Coach Frank," he heard a voice behind him on the bench, "let's drag out the booty music." Frank smiled but did not turn around.

Jenny was the poor mama who walked into the dugout with a hot dog for her son, and Frank hotly said, "Jenny, get that food out of here. These boys still have baseball to play." She looked face slapped when she turned and walked out of the dugout. Frank heard her husband, Tim, say, "I told you that wasn't going to work."

Big G had played for Frank during the regular season and sang out, "Rain, rain, go away, come again another day!" There was nervous laughter among the boys, but mostly they sat there stone-faced and watched sheets of rain flood the field. Big Train sat at the end of the dugout and stared at his feet with an icy glare. He still gripped a baseball.

When Doc pointed out the Eastonola team was out of their dugout, playing slip-and-slide in the rain, the thunder and lightning had long left the area, and the rain itself was subsiding. There were pools of water everywhere.

"Coach," Mark, the catcher, asked Frank, "why are they over there playing in the water?"

"Because," Frank said, "their coach thinks the game is going to be postponed because the field is too wet to play on. He thinks we'll come back out here tomorrow."

"You think that's going to happen?" asked Adam. One day, Adam would play on two national championship teams for the University of South Carolina.

"Nope," Frank said. "We'll finish this tonight. This old field was built to drain water."

No sooner were the words out of Frank's mouth than an umpire walked up to Frank and spoke through the fence. "They need about thirty minutes to fix the field, and we'll finish up."

Frank turned to his bench.

"This is why you don't play in the rain or have a hot dog supper," Frank said sharply. "We are ready to go back out on the field; Eastonola over there, well, their coach must now get them game ready all over again. Goofy and baseball don't mix."

Frank rubbed his hands absentmindedly but heard Big G say, "Coach Frank looks like a mad scientist."

Sugarman said, "I think he's crazy."

There were no motivational speeches when the game resumed. Every boy on Frank's team knew they were very close to seeing their baseball season come to an end.

Leading off the bottom of the fifth, down 3-1, was Matthew. He singled on a 2-2 pitch. Hammer, the first baseman, singled. Daryl, who had pitched the complete-game win the day before, was hit by a pitch to load the bases. Mark, the catcher, singled in Matthew, and J-Bird singled, scoring Hammer. The game was tied 3-3, with no outs. Calvin's leadoff walk scored Daryl, and the Concord All-Stars went ahead 4-3. Todd then singled in Mark. When Adam grounded out to second, he scored Jay. When the damage was done, with water still dripping from the top of the dugouts, Concord's All-Stars had gone up 6-3.

The teams changed places for the sixth and final inning, and Frank caught his pitcher as he left the dugout. He pulled out the oversized whistle and gave three long, slow blasts on it. Aaron's smile showed up ever so briefly. "Nail it down for us, Big Train." The pitcher nodded but never spoke.

As the first hitter stepped into the batter's box, Doc shouted, "Bring the wind, Big Train! Bring the wind!"

Eastonola never knew what ran over them.

Aaron faced three hitters and struck out all three – the last one watched a fastball explode by him for strike three. When the umpire called him out, Mark tossed his mask from behind the plate and descended on the pitcher's mound with his friends. Aaron had thrown only eleven pitches to retire those three hitters, and nine had been heat-seeking strikes.

After a team photograph with the championship trophy, the boys were chased away by the return of rain, but as they ran off the field, Doc hollered, "Have all the hot dogs you want, boys. Coach Frank is buying." Frank smiled as he went to apologize to the mom he had thrown out of the dugout.

⚾ ⚾ ⚾

Neither the Marlins nor the Braves scored in the fifth inning, and the Braves still led 2-0. John Smoltz, a future Braves Hall of Famer, was throwing a gem for the home team.

Bradley and Whitney stood up and started up the steps. She still wore Frank's jacket, and he was glad she was making use of it. When they were out of earshot, Phil whispered, "Can you believe she's with him?"

Frank smiled, thinking of the time he and Vicki walked into a restaurant and he heard someone say the same thing of him. Frank didn't answer Phil and was hoping the salesmen would get bored with the game and leave.

SIXTH INNING
THE MIRACLE IN MAY .

There was a little froggy
Sitting on a loggy
Cheering for the other team
He had no sense at all
Fell into the water
Bumped his little head
When he got up, this is what he said
"Go, Go, Go. Go you mighty Shark attack
Fight, Fight, Fight. Fight you mighty Shark attack
Win, Win, Win. Win you mighty Shark attack
Go, Fight, Win!
Crush their faces in!"

The sprinkle at Turner Field had ended and now returned – not so much a rain, but a misting. Bradley and Whitney returned to their seats, and Frank heard Bradley say, "I'm not sure we're staying out here just to get wet." The couple behind Frank was rustling around, pulling plastic ponchos out of a bag and putting them on. The man was fussing about it, but his wife kept insisting he not get cold and wet for fear of catching a cold.

"You'll end up in the hospital," she fussed.

"I'm too mean to get sick," he retorted.

Before starting the sixth inning, the Braves showed video highlights from their games of past seasons on a large jumbotron in the outfield. Second only to Henry Aaron's 715th career home run on April 8, 1975, most Braves fans agreed was winning game seven of the 1992 National League Championship Series against the Pittsburgh Pirates.

The series was knotted three games each in the best of seven championship series, and the Pirates led 2-0 going into the bottom of the ninth inning of the championship game. The Braves needed two to tie and three to win, or their season would be over. After scoring one run and with two outs, the Braves had the bases loaded for bench player Francisco Cabrera. Cabrera singled to left, scoring David Justice from third to tie the game. But to the amazement of a worldwide audience, first baseman Sid Bream, who had been on second, ran right through third and followed Justice to the plate with the winning run. Superstar left fielder Barry Bonds had played Cabrera's hit and threw it home to Pirates catcher Mike LaValliere. The throw was slightly off target, allowing Bream to slide just out of LaValliere's reach for the winning run. The Braves were launched into the World Series.

As the video played on the large screen, Whitney said, "I bet that was exciting to see when it happened."

Frank said, "I was sitting in our front room. My wife and young sons had gone to bed. When Bream scored that run, I ran into the yard and just started screaming, 'Braves win! Braves win!' It was fantastic."

She laughed because Frank had thrown his arms into the air, recreating the drama that had occurred in his front yard.

"It was a miracle," he said, emphatically, as if she had missed God's parting of the Red Sea.

As the video went black before announcing the first Marlins batter of the sixth inning, Frank thought about another game he still regarded as a miracle – only this one happened in Concord, South Carolina, at the Dixie ballpark.

⚾ ⚾ ⚾

There were two miracles during that special Concord baseball season, no, three.

⚾ ⚾ ⚾

The first miracle was not an event, but the coming of a person. He was miraculous and just what the Sharks needed. This miracle came in the form of a short redheaded rooster of a man who came to the year's first practice with his son. His black Ford F-250 loudly barked as he parked it alongside minivans and extra-large SUVs in the outer limits of the Field of Dream's left field. Frank, Doc, and the gathering players all stopped to watch the loud truck park.

What emerged from the driver's side belied the size of the vehicle, but not the spectacle. The door blew open, and Willet J. Wood hopped to the ground. It was immediately clear that he needed every bit of the driver's-side access rail to get into the vehicle; to get out, he honestly jumped out. He landed squarely on both feet, reached behind the driver's seat, and removed a cap and glove. Raking his red hair back, he donned the cap and started for the practice gathering.

"Come on, Little Wood," he shouted over his shoulder to a boy just as tall as his daddy. Then, as he walked toward Frank's truck, he shouted toward the coaches and players, "Here come the Woods, here come the Woods!"

"Dear Lord," Frank said.

"Agreed," Doc said. "Who the heck is this? Were you drunk at the draft?"

Frank had drafted Little Wood in a late round. By that point in the draft, Frank was looking for boys who could catch a fly ball in the outfield, and the boy proved in the league player assessment that he could do that. Unfortunately, and laughably, the boy's mother, Wynette, had brought him to the assessment. The boy's dad, who now swaggered up to Frank and Doc, had worked during the player assessment and missed it.

Frank now knew why there were snickers when he drafted Little Wood.

"Who in the wide, wide world of sports is Coach Frank?" the man stopped and shouted.

Frank nervously raised his hand but hoped Doc might raise his hand too.

"Coach, this here is my boy Little Wood – his name is Willie J, but you can call him Little Wood," the man said. "My name is Willet J. Wood." He extended his hand, which was more of a stump because his little hands were, well, so little. Frank had average-sized hands, and in the handshake, Frank seemed to swallow him.

Before Frank or Doc could say anything, Willet J. Wood bowed up.

"My friends call me Pecker," he said proudly.

There was stunned silence.

Frank stared at him. Doc began laughing – not so much at the man's nickname but Frank's stoic, unbelieving, shocked reaction. Frank had even removed his sunglasses to rub his eyes.

"That's right," the little man said, reluctantly but resigned to the fact. "Pecker Wood."

Several of the players, Sugarman, JP, Hammer, Sarge – the squad veterans – exploded into snickering laughter as they picked up baseballs to warm up their arms before practice.

"It's alright, boys," Pecker said. "It's been my nickname my whole life. I know it's funny. I played a little ball; everyone has a nickname. You can laugh. I know there's no disrespect intended."

Frank kept staring, speechless, now from behind his sunglasses – not entirely sure what to say.

"You mean that someone cheered you, as a kid, saying, 'Come on Pecker, take one deep?'" Doc asked, laughing.

Frank just shook his head.

"I sure would like to help you, Coach," Pecker said toward Frank. It was almost pitiful – like the little rooster had known a lot of rejection over the years. Frank saw it; Doc saw it too.

Frank sighed, and Pecker saw the grim look on his face even if the sunglasses blocked Frank's eyes. Frank was only six feet tall, a little overweight, but he dwarfed the man. Doc, who was six three and rail skinny was like a giant.

"It will mean so much to me to be out here and help you and to be able to walk this path with my son," Pecker said. "I'll stay out of the way; you men tell me where I can help you. I'll do whatever you ask. I promise, I'll be your best cheerleader."

Doc could stand it no longer. "We'd be honored, Pecker." Then he burst out laughing.

Frank sighed deeply. His navy-blue hat with the white S was pulled down on his forehead, and the mirrored sunglasses shielded his eyes. "Alright. But around these boys, I'm calling you Coach or Willet. I am not going to call you Pecker for the next two years. I refuse to do that."

"Fair enough," the man said, smiling and looking around at the snickering boys. He shook his head, affirming that he had been accepted. "Thank you, thank you."

Doc hopped off the tailgate and said to Frank, "I am definitely calling him Pecker. It's going to be a great season." He smiled.

"I'm sure we'll never forget it," Frank said.

Pecker was the first to arrive at the Field of Dreams each day. He hooked an old drag to the back of his truck and smoothed out the infield. When Frank noticed the outfield grass needed cutting that spring, it miraculously received a trimming. Someone said Pecker had been out there early one morning, before he went to work, cutting the outfield grass.

What's more, it became clear that Pecker knew very little about baseball, but he knew a great deal about being left behind or left out. Every practice, he migrated toward the boys who had been late draft picks, couldn't throw well, couldn't catch well, and couldn't hit well. He befriended them, standing among them in the outfield and cheering them on. He used an old sawed-off tennis racket to hit tennis balls high in the air to help boys learn to catch pop flies. When one of them had the slightest measure of success, Pecker shouted, "Atta boy!" as loud as possible and sometimes did a backflip, landing perfectly on both feet every time. He even began calling the little group of outfielders "his boys," and the boys responded to the colorful, cartoon man who always cheered them.

To his face and behind his back, Doc praised Pecker's arrival to the team as a miracle – the missing piece of the Sharks coaching staff. Doc had witnessed Frank's intensity, especially at practice, and knew Pecker was the perfect counterbalance to it. With himself positioned somewhere in the middle, he often said it was a perfect coaching unit.

⚾ ⚾ ⚾

Doc was hitting infield during one practice while Frank pulled the pitchers aside to let them each throw a short bullpen. Frank had developed theories about control pitching based on how a player's hips opened up and his lead foot planted when coming down on the mound. He was constantly preaching the front foot's careful landing and bringing the knees close together as the body came forward. Frank preached that his young pitchers focus more on control than velocity.

"If you walk two in a row, you are done," Frank said. "Once you lose control in a game, it's gone. You won't get it back.

"Right now, at your age, this is a game about contact," Frank said – often shouted so even the mamas in their oversized SUVs could hear him in left field. "We *want them* to hit it and let our defense make plays, or we want them to strike out. Throw strikes – don't worry about how hard you throw it. That will come in later years. We are playing for today, not when you play for the high school team."

He was in the middle of teaching when he noticed Pecker standing behind him. Aggravated at the interruption, he swiveled while sitting on an overturned mud bucket that he sat on while catching his pitchers.

"Coach Frank," Pecker began. "We've got a problem. John-Henry has disappeared."

Frank stood up. "What?"

"He went into the woods and hasn't come back."

When Frank's Sharks first began practicing at the Field of Dreams, it didn't take long for boys to need an opportunity to relieve themselves. The thick, pine woods behind first base provided lots of privacy for boys – and coaches, and some parents – to find quick privacy.

Frank had even walked the entire team into the woods, showing them the general area where they could go when nature called. He had nailed an orange construction flag to a tree.

"Don't go any further than this," he said. "This is far enough." He pointed back to the field, which was barely visible through the underbrush of the woods. "You have plenty of privacy right here. All of us go to the bathroom the same way, so there's no need to be embarrassed. Just tell a coach you are running to the woods."

John-Henry, one of Pecker's outfielders, had asked for permission to visit the woods, and Pecker had sent him along. Frank had noticed the boy run past him into the woods and thought nothing of it. Boys were constantly running back and forth to the woods.

"John-Henry!" Frank shouted in the direction of the orange flag, which was barely visible.

There was no response.

Frank tossed his catcher's mitt on the ground and started into the woods toward the general area where he knew most of the team visited. When he got there, there was no John-Henry. He swore under his breath.

Pecker was right behind him. Most of the team had abandoned practice to follow too.

"John-Henry!" Frank shouted. There was no response.

John-Henry was a slight boy given to daydreaming. Each of the coaches had, at various times, called John-Henry to focus or pay attention, for his safety. Some of the boys on the team could hit and throw hard, and it was important for boys on the field to pay attention.

The entire team, including Doc, now stood around the pine trees underneath the orange flag.

"John-Henry!" Frank shouted again. The boys began chanting too. "Alright, boys, we don't need a search party. Doc is going to take you back to the field and continue practice. Coach Willet and I will look for John-Henry." Disgruntled, the team followed Doc back to the field.

"Where do you think that boy went?" Pecker asked Frank and to himself at the same time. "You don't reckon there's an old well out here he could have fallen into, do you?"

"Dear Lord, I hope not," Frank said. He started walking deeper into the woods, past the orange flag. Pecker was alongside him.

"Look here, Frank," the assistant said, pushing through some fallen tree branches. He picked up John Henry's baseball glove. "He was here, alright. Now where did he go?"

"John-Henry!" Frank shouted. "Son, if you can hear me, you had better let me know it right now." There was both anger and a touch of panic in his voice. "Let's fan out. You go right, and I'll go left."

Frank walked alone, quickly, for about twenty yards before the woods opened to a mobile home park, where ten single-wide mobile homes were anchored – five on each side of a narrow dirt drive. Frank heard children playing and decided to see if any of them had seen his errant outfielder.

As he came from behind and around one of the mobile homes, he spotted the children playing kickball in the dirt drive. Right there among them was John-Henry, having the time of his life.

"John-Henry!" Frank shouted, and the boy snapped to attention. He stared at his head coach, who was not smiling.

"Hey, Coach," the boy said, waving. "Will you tell my mama just to pick me up over here. I'm going to play here today."

Frank stared at him. The boy continued smiling at him. "They have water if I get thirsty."

"No, you are not playing here," Frank said, walking to the boy. "You are coming with me." Frank was angry – hot – as if he was talking to one of his boys. "If you were my son, I would wear you out right now. You wouldn't sit down for a week. John-Henry, you scared us to death." He marched the boy back through the woods, shouting for Pecker to hear, "I found him."

After practice, Frank had a long talk with John-Henry's parents, and from that day forward John Henry's dad was in the outfield shagging balls at every practice.

Frank also made sure he or one of the coaches kept better tabs on who went to the woods and visited the orange flag.

⚾ ⚾ ⚾

One evening, at the close of practice, as the boys packed up their equipment and ran for their parents' vehicles in the outfield, Frank, Doc, and Pecker stood around the tailgate and talked about the next game on the team's schedule. It was Doc who changed the subject.

"So if you don't mind me asking," Doc said to Pecker, "how did you get that nickname? I know it's not because you are a Pecker Wood yourself." Pecker looked at him funny, knowing full well that most Southerners used the term to describe a poor, illiterate white person.

"Welp," Pecker said, "you see this mop of hair? My daddy said I reminded him of a woodpecker – redheaded and annoying as hell." He laughed so hard he hollered and poked Frank in the ribs. "I'm aggravating, I know I am, but it's all in good fun. I couldn't help that my last name is Wood. Pecker Wood." He shrugged his shoulders.

⚾ ⚾ ⚾

The second miracle that season arrived via third base. JP had been Frank's third baseman the year before, and Frank had imagined him moving over to shortstop for the current season. That would allow Frank to toggle Sugarman and Hammer from pitcher to catcher during each game. Sarge, a lockdown second baseman, provided defense up the middle. With his defense and pitching generally set, Frank used his first-round draft pick on a sturdy boy who was a natural first baseman and power hitter. His second-round pick was a tall, motorized boy named Tyler, who could run like the wind. Frank put him in center field and told him "to catch everything but a bad cold."

"If our boy Pecker can get that outfield in good shape, I think we'll win some games this year," Doc said. "We might not win the division, but we'll have a winning season."

"Can we just call him Willet?" Frank asked.

"No," Doc said. "How many times in your life are you gonna be able to call someone Pecker and have their permission to do it?"

Just before opening day, around mid-March, Frank scheduled a customary preseason scrimmage. Even back to his days in Jenson, preseason scrimmages helped coaches test-drive the defenses they had imagined and let the boys play some baseball rather than just attend practices every day.

Frank's defensive setup worked like clockwork, but he miscalculated what it meant bringing a tired catcher to the pitcher's mound as a closer. He decided to keep Hammer behind the plate and look for another pitcher. It was Sugarman who said to his coach, "Let JP have a chance."

Frank stared at his shortstop. He knew JP had the arm because Frank had seen the throws from third base the previous season. Frank just didn't know if JP could pitch, throwing with control while under pressure. JP was one of the team's biggest boys – not so much tall and not so much heavy, but just sizeable. He was quiet and determined and kind. He had a great demeanor for a pitcher. He worked hard, and he was surprised when Frank called him to the pitcher's mound at the close of a preseason scrimmage.

"I'm gonna let you close this scrimmage out for two innings," he said, and gave JP the ball.

"Me?" JP said, and smiled big. "Okay." Sugarman, now catching as Hammer moved to shortstop, was a good head shorter than JP, but the two were close friends.

"You got this, JP," Sugarman said. "It's just you and me playing catch." He turned and ran back behind home plate.

What happened next was nothing short of a miracle.

Frank stood behind the dugout fence.

JP rocked and fired, and the ball exploded out of his hand. It hit Sugarman's mitt with such force that the smaller boy recoiled into the legs of the umpire.

"Holy crap," Frank said quietly to himself. Then he looked at Doc. "This kid reminds me of Don Drysdale." Don Drysdale had been a power-throwing right-hander for the Los Angeles Dodgers in the 1960s. A big man, in 1968, he threw six consecutive shutout games. He was inducted into the Hall of Fame in 1984. Drysdale was on three World Series championship teams and was an All-Star nine times.

JP threw ten pitches that inning and struck out the side. When he went back out for the next inning, he fanned all three hitters he faced.

"My goodness, what a find," Doc said. "I never saw that coming."

When JP came off the field after the scrimmage was over, Frank gave him the scuffed-up game ball. "JP, don't ever forget this day. This is the day you became a baseball pitcher."

Decades later, Frank Wilcox opened an old U-Haul moving box full of old baseballs and removed them one by one. Some were signed by all the boys on a specific team, whether it was a competitive spring team or an instructional fall team. Some were game balls that his boys had earned during their playing days. Frank had jotted notes on others, marking his three hundredth game coaching or the seven hundredth spring game his sons had cumulatively played at the Concord ballpark.

He smiled when he held up one special ball. He had written these words in permanent black marker: "May 19 – The Miracle in May." He rolled the ball over and over in his hands. Of all the baseballs he owned, of all the memories, it was that game – that one game – that had been a magical miracle. He would never forget it.

◈ ◈ ◈

The best team in the league that season – the season Pecker Wood jumped out of that Ford F-250 and the year JP channeled Don Drysdale on the minor league pitcher's mound – was a team appropriately dressed in black, the Wolves. Their coach was a tall, unemotional, bearded man named Alex Coldstone. He had orchestrated one of the best, quietly audacious drafts in the Concord Dixie Youth League's history, assembling three lockdown pitchers, including a dynamic lefty with a quick release. Up and down that batting order, the Wolves could hit, and they had been drafted to run, and run they did. Speed was a significant part of their game. It was a complete team, and many of their opponents that year simply gave up, choosing to focus on the week's second game and being comfortable with a two-game split for the week.

Most coaches maintained a presence around the ballpark on Saturdays, watching the children of friends but also trying to watch their upcoming opponents play. It was all good fun to scout your opponents and know who could pitch and hit. After all, coaches voted on All-Stars at the end of the season, and knowing the players was important.

Frank had made a point of leaving practice early one day to watch the Wolves play. He was jealous of the talent up and down the lineup and how surgical they were at hitting and running and playing great defense. He admired Alex Coldstone, who always kept his composure. Frank prided himself on never being thrown out of a game, and Alex was of the same mindset.

After practice, Pecker and Little Wood joined Frank at the park, and the pair walked up with Frank's son tagging along with them. Each of them had a chicken finger basket, and Pecker handed a fourth supper basket to Frank.

"What's this?" Frank asked.

"Thought you might want some supper, Coach," Pecker said. Frank sighed at the kindness and watched as his son sat on the ground to eat the chicken fingers.

"Willet," Frank said, "you shouldn't have bought us supper. I don't have any cash with me to pay you back."

"Coach Frank, it's all God's money," Pecker said, smiling at him. "I'm just giving back to those the Lord loves. Besides, I'll bet there's a day when Little Wood here needs something, and you will be there to help him. We are all on the same team – the same family – which means we support one another. Enjoy your supper." He sat down and began to eat.

Frank smiled. A lesson was learned that he would never forget.

While Frank did take the occasional time to watch his upcoming opponents, Alex Coldstone took scouting nine- and ten-year-olds to a new level.

Frank's Sharks were defeating a decent Wildcat team 5-0. Frank noticed Alex sitting all alone, just beyond the center-field fence. He was dressed in black like his team's uniforms, a black baseball hat pulled low on his head, and a notebook in his lap. He sat there for the entire game, making sure everyone saw him studying the team, the coaching decisions, and the pitching and looking for slow infield play that gave his elite base runners an edge.

At one point during the game, Doc jogged out to center field to speak to Coldstone. The conversation was short, and when he returned to the dugout, Frank asked him about it.

"I just wanted him to know that we knew he was out here, and we were looking forward to Saturday's game against his team," Doc said. "He's creepy, Frank, and it's pretty bad when an undertaker calls someone else creepy. I think all of his clothes are black." He paused. "He wears black more than I do, and I get paid to wear black."

"I sure hope we beat them on Saturday," Frank said.

"Let's not kid ourselves," Doc whispered. "It will take a miracle."

⚾ ⚾ ⚾

It was a scorching-hot May that year, and the week of the games between the Wildcats and the Wolves, the thermostat went to ninety-five for several days. It felt like one hundred, and the shade gave no relief. Frank had to remind the boys to bring plenty of water with them to practice and games, and he made sure to have water with him just in case the boys needed more.

On Friday before the game against the Wolves, Frank called his team together around his truck's tailgate as practice ended at the Field of Dreams.

"We know what's ahead of us tomorrow," he said. "I'm not going to lie to you. We are still in a three-team race for our division championship. I wasn't sure we would be here this late in the season, but here we are. If we lose tomorrow, we've still had a great season, but we'll be eliminated from the race. If we win tomorrow, we are still in it. That's how it shakes out."

Frank had not pitched JP against the Wildcats, so he had his full rotation of pitchers available, but he also knew that the Wolves were never without pitching. And their lefty ace was available for the entire game.

"Boys," Doc said, "we just go out there and have fun, and we'll be just fine. I'll tell you something. Win or lose tomorrow, Santa Claus will still come on Christmas Eve. I believe in you, I believe you will do your best, and, well, goodness gracious, I believe in Santa Claus!"

There were several laughs from among the boys.

There was a cough from the back of the gathering. Frank looked up to see Pecker, who raised his hand, looking for permission to speak. Frank acknowledged him.

"Boys," the small man said, walking to the truck's tailgate so they could all face him. He turned his back to the tailgate and had to jump up to sit on it.

"I was never good at sports. My daddy didn't care about sports, so he never supported me. Everyone thought I was too little to be any good. But I'll tell you something, it's been a blessing to be out here with you boys and see how good you are, how hard you work, and how hard you try." He pointed to two boys who shared right field. "You two have worked as hard as any boys out here, and I believe tomorrow you are going to have a big day. Some of you boys don't hit so well, but you work hard, and I see it – we all see it. Don't think that you can't win tomorrow, because old Pecker says that yes you can."

⚾ ⚾ ⚾

The next day's game against the Wolves was at the end of the day, and there was nothing worse than playing at the end of a hot May Saturday when swimming pools and the nearby lake were calling one and all for a swim. Frank had prohibited swimming on game day but knew full well some of the boys went swimming ahead of a day's game. He just didn't want to know about it.

He had once encouraged a former team not to eat a big meal before a game. Still, Big G of that championship team confessed eating a big chili cheeseburger from Rush's restaurant before every game, and Frank could not argue with how well the boy hit the baseball afterward. Frank decided to mind his own business about pregame meals, or swimming, for that matter.

The game with the Wolves began at 7:05 p.m., five minutes late, because Frank had to pull John-Henry from a game of wall ball. The little boy had drifted there as the team walked to the dugout from taking pregame batting practice.

JP took the mound for Frank's Sharks, who were the home team. The big right-hander struck out three of the first four batters he faced, allowing one weak single. In the bottom of the first, Hammer walked for the Sharks and scored on Sugarman's base hit. Sugarman then stole his way around the bases and scored on a wild pitch before the side was retired on strikeouts. After one, the Sharks led 2-0.

⚾ ⚾ ⚾

The Wolves notched two triples to the fence in the top of the second but could only score one run. JP struck out two, and Sugarman, playing at short, got the third out on a 6-3 putout. The Sharks went 1, 2, 3 in the bottom of the second inning but still led 2-1.

⚾ ⚾ ⚾

JP got two quick outs in the top of the third but then faced the heart of the Wolves' order. He hit the third batter, gave up a single to the next one, and walked the next to load the bases. Frank walked out to the dugout.

JP stared at him.

"If they get too far ahead of us, we'll need a miracle to win it," Frank said. He immediately regretted the negative mojo, remembering an alleged story about Hall of Fame pitcher Nolan Ryan, who gave up a home run after his coach came to the mound and said, "Don't give up a home run."

The next hitter drilled a three-run double, giving the Wolves a 4-2 lead as one of their fans shouted, "We're on track now, boys. Let 'em have it."

The next hitter popped up weakly to JP for the third out.

In the bottom of the third, the Sharks had runners at second and third with one out and could not score either. After three, the Sharks were down 4-2.

As the Sharks gathered their gloves to take the field for the top of the fourth, Pecker took JP by the shoulder. "Son, you go out there and throw mean." He shaped his face into an angry look. "Blow that seed right by them."

And that's just what JP did. He struck out all three hitters he faced.

In the bottom of the fourth, with one out, Tyler singled up the middle for the Sharks but was thrown out at second trying to stretch it for a double.

Frank met him coming off the field. "You would have been safe if you had not paused at first."

"Coach, I was waiting on Doc to tell me to go," Tyler said.

Frank turned toward the entire dugout, "Boys, we are a running team. The base coach is there to stop you and not start you. Unless me or Doc, one of us, tells you to stop, you keep going as hard as you can go. We will tell you when to stop – not when to go."

"Lord, we need a miracle to win this game," Pecker said out loud, to himself, and as a prayer all at the same time.

And at that very minute, lightning streaked across the dark South Carolina sky. Thunder boomed.

The rain came – not heavy – but steady.

Doc looked at Frank, remembering the Rosewood All-Star game, and laughed. "Are you kidding me, Frank?"

Frank shook his head.

Chaos, the likes of which had never been seen before, ensued.

According to the league rules, a game was official after four of six innings were played. With two outs in the bottom of the fourth, the Sharks could have been down to their last out. The umpires could have rightly ordered everyone on the field, in the rain, and played for one more out to end the fourth inning. With the fourth inning over, the game called official because of rainout, the Wolves would have won 4-2.

But the umpires wavered. They rightly sent everyone to the dugouts with lightning but instructed no one to leave the complex.

Normally stoic, Alex Coldstone lost his mind. He started shouting at the umpires to finish it. "Let's finish it right now!"

Seeking shelter and wanting to flee Alex, the umpires retreated to Frank's dugout. Frank had long befriended the men in blue for a moment in time such as this.

"We can't play with lightning," Frank said calmly. "We can't send these boys back out there in a storm. None of us want that liability." Truthfully, there had only been that one lightning burst. Now it was just a light, steady rain.

Alex Coldstone was now outside Frank's dugout, standing in the rain, begging to finish the game. Frank pointed to first base and the puddle that was forming there.

"We can play, Frank," Alex said, disgusted. "We practice in the rain all the time. All we need is one or two hitters, and this can be over for the week. We can start preparing for next week."

Frank looked at the home plate umpire and said calmly, "We can also finish it tomorrow afternoon when the sun is shining."

"No one wants to come back out here on Sunday," Alex moaned. "Come on, Frank. Come on, blue."

"I LOOOVEEE Sunday baseball," Pecker crowed. "I'd rather watch Sunday baseball than any other day of the week." He continued providing background noise, and Alex turned on him.

"Who are you anyway?" he asked the small redhead.

"Pecker Wood," he said proudly, and for a minute, Alex thought he was being insulted.

Frank said, "No, Alex, *his name really is* Pecker Wood. It's a long story."

One of the umpires laughed, but another one said, "Look, this is a really good game. We have water on the field, it's still raining, and it's getting late. We've seen lightning. Let's come back tomorrow at 2:00 p.m. and finish it. I'd like to see it finished."

Alex stormed back to his dugout, and Frank said, "Sack up the equipment. Let's go home."

⚾⚾⚾

The sun was out the next day, and by 2:00 p.m., it was already ninety-five degrees with a heat index boiling over one hundred. The two teams arrived and took warm-ups as if they had six full innings to play – not just one batter left in the fourth and two more full innings after that.

The home plate umpire ensured the Wolves defense was set as it had been the day before. He double-checked the Sharks batting order and double-checked to make sure the right batter came to the plate. The scoreboard read 4-2 in favor of the Wolves and showed it was the fourth inning with two outs.

The Sharks sent their third baseman to the plate, and he struck out swinging on a full count.

"Whew," Frank said under his breath. "I'm glad that didn't happen last night. This game would be over."

Doc looked to the heavens.

⚾ ⚾ ⚾

Something curious had happened to JP overnight. Perhaps he got a good night's sleep. Perhaps he wasn't tired after lounging all day on a Saturday before a night game. Perhaps he felt the touch of the Lord at the Lutheran church that morning. Perhaps he just didn't have pitcher's jitters from the day before.

Whatever happened to JP, he came out throwing heat. He struck out two of the three hitters he faced in the top of the fifth, and the third attempted a bunt, which Hammer played perfectly from behind the plate, throwing to Sarge, who came over from second and covered first base for the out.

The Sharks mustered nothing in the bottom of the fifth; three of the four hitters struck out to the Wolves' pitching. Going to the sixth and final inning, the Wolves still led 4-2.

⚾ ⚾ ⚾

In the top of the sixth, JP fanned the leadoff hitter on three pitches. The next Wolves hitter grounded out to Sarge at second. The third hitter singled past first base before the cleanup hitter grounded out to second for the third out. Relieved, the Sharks ran off the field and into their dugout. Every boy coming off the field knew the team had dodged a bullet against one of the best-hitting and best-coached teams in the league.

"Alright, boys," Frank said. "This is it. We got three outs to score three runs and win this game."

"Or two runs and tie it," Hammer said.

"Let's win it," Frank said, winking at his catcher.

The Wolves' pitcher saw the win in sight, and so did his coach.

"This game is ours," Alex Coldstone said from the dugout, but loud enough for everyone to hear. "Let's get out of here quick, 1, 2, 3.

That's how it started. The Sharks sent their first two hitters to the plate, and both grounded out to second base. Down to their final out and behind two runs, the Sharks dugout was "like a funeral home with no business," Doc said.

The Wolves dugout was rocking. Boys in the dugout were on the fence, shaking it. Parents were standing, and some were packing up their folding chairs, believing the game was already over. Only one more out until this two-day saga was over.

Sugarman, whose defense often secured his spot on postseason All-Star teams, was up for the Sharks, and he singled. JP then walked. The Wolves pitcher was a bit rattled and walked Tyler to load the bases with two outs. Alex Coldstone made an uncharacteristic pitching change, and Frank could sense that the Wolves looked worried in the hot May sunshine.

Frank was sending up the boy who had struck out to end the controversial fourth.

"Don't worry about the last time," Frank said calmly and just above a whisper. "They know you struck out before. They expect it.

Put the bat on the ball and see what happens. Or, as my daddy used to say to me, 'Put the bat on the ball and run like hell.'" The boy nodded his head, and Frank knew full well that the boy's nerves had stopped any words from reaching his ears. The boy just wanted to get this over with or vomit.

On the first pitch, the little boy put the ball in play to short, and the shortstop looked to his left, but the second baseman was slow moving to the base for the 6-4 putout. The shortstop panicked and threw the ball home to the catcher, but bounced it, and Sugarman scored easily for the Sharks. The bases remained loaded on the errant fielder's choice. The score was 4-3 in favor of the Wolves. The tying run was at third, the winning run at second.

Momentum had shifted mightily toward the Sharks.

Frank saw that Sarge, his serious-minded second baseman, was coming to bat. Sarge had already struck out twice in the game. Frank and Doc had worked with the boy to draw a walk or bunt, and Sarge became a very good bunter. Against great league pitching, Sarge often used the unexpected bunt to reach first base.

"You know what we need, right?" Frank asked him, and Sarge shook his head that he understood. He was all business. Coaching third base, Frank told JP, "If he gets the ball down, you take off and slide in clean and hard. We may be able to tie the game."

Sarge took one strike.

The ballfield was deathly silent. Doc looked around. "I feel like we should all sing, 'How Great Thou Art' and bury something." The Wolves fans had sat back down on the bleachers.

Pecker shouted to the team's fans, "Let's go, show these boys some support." The Sharks fans began shouting encouragement to their second baseman. The Wolves players had never had this kind of opposition – all their games had been pretty one-sided victories. Pecker had the Sharks on the fence of the dugout, screaming for their teammates on the bases.

The roof, the roof, the roof is on fire!

We don't need no water, let the flames go higher!

The pitch came in as a perfect strike, and Sarge squared to bunt. The ball met the bat and rolled into a devil's triangle between the pitcher's mound and first base. It was the spot where bunts disappeared into hits. The ball was too far for the catcher or pitcher to get it and make a play. The first baseman couldn't leave the base and get back. Sarge bolted out of the batter's box. Frank's eyes were fixed on Sarge – his short legs churning down that base path as the pitcher ran for the ball. JP charged home and slid in uncontested to tie the game at 4-4.

Tyler, who went on to play local high school baseball, was on second when Sarge bunted that ball, and he took off for third. As directed, he watched for Frank to stop him, but Frank was watching Sarge and never saw his center fielder coming around third. Tyler streaked past his coach on the way home.

Sarge beat the pitcher's throw to first by half a shoe, and when Frank saw umpire Jimmy Hood's arms wave as a "Safe!" call, he only then noticed Tyler had scored the winning run.

"It's a miracle!" Pecker shouted from the dugout, and Frank collapsed to his knees in the third base coaching box. "We've all seen a baseball miracle!"

Just behind Frank, in the Wolves dugout, Alex Coldstone said loud enough for Frank to hear him: "This was never right, Frank.

We should have finished yesterday." Frank paid no attention but ran to his team, pouring out of the dugout.

The Sharks didn't win the division championship that season, but they finished 13-7 while hitting only .225 as a team. On defense, in twenty games, the team only made seven errors. For many years, Frank said that season was his best coaching job and solidified his belief that pitching and defense can always win games.

And having a Miracle in May didn't hurt either.

Neither the Braves nor the Marlins scored in the sixth inning, and the Braves still led 2-0. The rain had subsided for the night.

SEVENTH INNING
THE FIRST BASEMAN, THE FOX,
AND A PRAYER

I see a hole out there; I see a hole out there
I see an H-O-L-E hole out there
So hit the ball out there, so hit the ball out there
So hit the B-A-L-L ball out there

It was the seventh inning, and while the famed seventh-inning stretch came at the midpoint of the inning, there was a Frank Wilcox tradition that occurred at this point of Braves games that he saw in person.

"Well," he announced rather loudly, "the seventh inning means it's time for seventh inning Dippin' Dots." The little boys in front of Frank heard him and immediately jumped out of their seats.

"Dippin' Dots!"

Their dad turned to Frank and said, "Thanks a lot, pal."

"Come with me, dad; we'll buy Dots for everyone," Frank said.

The man stood up as the boys cheered and shouted, "Chocolate! Large!" The large-sized Dippin' Dots came in a small, overturned plastic Braves helmet. The two men made their way to the left, meeting in the aisle.

Frank turned back to his small baseball community. "Anyone like Dippin' Dots?"

Whitney sheepishly raised her hand and said, "Chocolate, please." Bradley shook his head no and held up a half-finished beer. Frank stared at him, thinking, "I wish you had played for me as a kid." The older couple behind Frank smiled, and Frank asked, "Chocolate or cookies 'n' cream?" They both wanted chocolate.

Phil whined, "Hey, what about me?"

Frank asked, "What'll it be?"

"I'll be the oddball; I'll take the cookies and cream," he said.

"You got it, Phil," Frank said, pointing to him.

It didn't take long to find the Dippin' Dots, and Frank bought dots for Whitney, Phil, and the older couple, while the dad bought Dots for his group.

As they settled up with a young man under the Dippin' Dots umbrella, Frank said, "This all started when my son Richard and I came to games together. He's grown now, and our motto is that we buy a ticket in and then eat our way out. We bought some kind of concession at the start of every odd inning, and Dippin' Dots was assigned to the seventh."

"I don't know if I could afford to eat that much," the dad said.

"I don't come to many games," Frank laughed. "Do you coach your boys?"

The dad said he did coach them. He was proud of them. One was a pretty good glove at shortstop, and the other was the first baseman.

"I didn't play much as a kid," Frank said. "But when I did play, I usually played first base."

"My boy was an accidental first baseman," the dad said. "We needed a first baseman, and I converted him over there from third base. We were desperate for a glove over there, and he was my best alternative."

Frank smiled. He knew all about desperately needing a first baseman.

⚾ ⚾ ⚾

The man who nicknamed his only son Pecker, well, was graveyard dead.

Doc called that January morning to tell Frank the news and to encourage Frank to attend the hurried funeral the next day. Frank anticipated the supporters and well-wishers would be few, and he made plans to be at the funeral home by 2:30 p.m.

"Was it sudden?" Frank asked Doc through the telephone.

"Well, not as sudden as this funeral service seems to be," Doc said. "I mean, at least give the family and friends time to see his well-groomed postmortem body. They are rushing this good man into the ground." Realizing he hadn't answered Frank's question, he continued, "He had been sick for quite some time. I think Pecker's taking it pretty hard."

⚾ ⚾ ⚾

When he parked at the large funeral home, Frank knew his guess had been correct. The funeral service was scheduled to start in thirty minutes, and the parking lot was empty. Pecker's Ford F-250, freshly cleaned and polished, was parked just beside the door marked Visitors.

Frank walked inside, and Doc was there to meet him.

"You clean up pretty good," Doc said to Frank, shaking his friend's hand. "The family is already in the chapel." Out of the vestibule, to the right, Frank walked down a brown-carpeted path to open doors through which the low, dreadful sound of a funeral organ played. Frank stepped into the chapel and immediately saw the slumped shoulders of his friend; the red, uncombed hair was splashed over the top of Pecker's head. Frank sat on the pew behind him and touched Pecker's shoulder. The short man, usually so loud and proud, was subdued and resigned to grief.

"Hey, Coach," he said, barely above a whisper. "Thanks for coming."

"I'm sorry to hear about your daddy, Willet," Frank said. "Is there anything Vicki and I can do for you over the next few days? Do you need help with Little Wood?"

Pecker shook his head. "No, sir." Tears filled his eyes, and Frank thought they might just flood down the man's face for a minute. "He wasn't a good daddy, but I'll miss him."

Frank put his hand on Pecker's shoulder and left it there. "Doc and I aren't going to let you walk this valley alone, I promise."

"Coach," he said, "do you think my daddy's in heaven?"

Frank took a big deep breath. "I don't know, Willet. Did your daddy love Jesus?"

"He did love Jesus," Pecker said. "He wasn't fond of churches, though, and right now, he's probably wondering when I'm going to get him out of this one and on into the ground."

"If he loved Jesus, he's in heaven," Frank said. Then, he couldn't resist. "Willet, if you love Jesus, you will see your daddy again one day."

"Thank you, Coach. Thank you for saying that," he said. "I do love the Lord. I love him more than anyone."

Frank smiled and patted his shoulder just about the time Little Wood and the rest of Pecker's family arrived for the service.

"I'll keep you all in prayer, Willet," Frank said, standing to shake Little Wood's hand and give Wynette a hug.

Pecker shifted in his seat so he could see Frank's face.

"You better pray we get a first baseman," he said. "We got an All-Star infield but no one for them to throw to at first base." Frank smiled and knew his friend was going to be just fine.

⚾ ⚾ ⚾

Pecker was right.

The Sharks had four players coming back from a team that had only won five games. Those four players represented a strong infield: Hoss at third, E-Mar at short, Crime Dog or just "Dog" at second, and Cody behind the plate. There was no first baseman. Frank had a good draft, but none of the selections was tall enough or athletic enough to play first.

"I'm not sure how you sat through a two-hour draft and came away without a first baseman," Doc had said at the team's first practice, surveying the boys at the Field of Dreams. "Were you asleep? Did you step out for a telephone call?"

"You weren't praying hard enough," Pecker said, overhearing the conversation. He folded his hands under his chin and leaned back, crowing as loud as he could, "Lord, right here at this lovely Field of Dreams, we beseech you, Lord, to send us a first baseman. We'll take a righty, but we would prefer a lefty as long as we're asking."

Frank rolled his eyes as Doc smiled.

"But thy will be done," Pecker said, reminding the good Lord that He was in charge.

Frank chuckled to see several of the boys bowing their heads in prayer, not completely sure what was happening, but happy to bow reverently for what they perceived was a serious conversation with the Almighty.

"Boys, it's okay," Doc said to end the prayer meeting. "Let's start throwing; let's loosen those arms."

Doc put on his glove and trotted toward first base, saying, "I'll play first until the Lord answers Pecker's prayer," and then under his breath, "or strikes us all dead for blasphemy."

⚾ ⚾ ⚾

A gruff firefighter who had coached several years in the Concord league had told Frank early in the Concord season of his coaching life, "Don't panic at what you see during the first week of practice. One or two of them will probably quit, and then you can go back to the pool for the late registrations."

It was somewhat true. As fun as Frank and Doc made their practices, there was always a late-round pick or two who decided competitive baseball – even at nine and ten – wasn't for them. There were lots of reasons for a boy to quit. Some quit because of the five practices each week. Baseball infringed on other activities like Scouts, and for some, the time commitment was too much for parents. Many late-round picks realized they didn't want to play baseball.

Frank was fond of telling parents in the fall league and at his pre-season parent meetings, "Passion is nontransferable. I don't care how much you love a hobby or activity, or how good you were at it; that doesn't mean your child will love it or be good at it. You can steer them in a direction, but sooner or later they will turn it where they want to go." He had seen many former college players push their boys to play baseball only to be frustrated when the boys wanted to quit or do something different.

After one week of practice at the Field of Dreams that year, one of the boys didn't show up, and his mama called Frank to say her son was taking guitar lessons instead. She wanted to see if Frank could help her get a refund from the league.

"I always wanted to play the guitar, and so I admire your son for wanting to pursue that," Frank said. "He can play the guitar for the rest of his life. He certainly won't play baseball for the rest of his life." He pledged to help her get the money refunded from the league.

⚾⚾⚾

The guitar player's loss meant an open roster spot, and Frank let the league office know.

He nervously told the league official, "We've been praying for a first baseman."

The league official gave Frank the name and telephone number of a family that had just moved to Concord. The dad was a salesman. The boy's name was Lance.

"Do you know if he's ever played before?" Frank asked.

"I don't know," the league official said. "Maybe you can teach him to play first base if that's what you need."

At the Field of Dreams later that day, Frank shared the news with Doc and the rest of the team. None of the boys knew the player, Lance, from school. Frank told them he would call the family that night.

"Shall we gather over at first base for a word with the Almighty?" Pecker asked, and Frank waved him off in fake disgust.

"It's not a bad idea," Doc whispered so only Frank could hear it. "We won five games last year, and I think we might win six as things stand right now. That missing puzzle piece is the difference between a finished puzzle and a frustratingly incomplete mess."

⚾ ⚾ ⚾

Frank made the call that evening.

Lance's dad answered the telephone. The family had just moved to Concord within the past month and was eager to get their son involved with other children beyond school. The dad said that Lance was a soccer player first and foremost, and he would play in an instructional spring league. But, what the heck, they thought he might enjoy baseball too.

Frank's heart sank.

"Well I need to tell you about baseball in Concord," Frank began. "We practice four to five times per week and have two games per week. My team usually takes off on Wednesday and Sunday, but sometimes we have a little optional batting practice on Sunday afternoon."

"That's kid's baseball?" the dad asked. "Wow, I'm not sure we can commit to that insanity. Besides, he's first and foremost a soccer player."

"That's not a problem, except that to play for me in this league, your son will have to be first and foremost a baseball player in the spring," Frank said.

The wrangling continued for another ten minutes before Lance's dad agreed to bring him to the team's next practice. He chuckled when Frank told him they practiced behind a church on an old field nicknamed the Field of Dreams.

⚾ ⚾ ⚾

No player in Frank Wilcox's Sharks' history was ever as anticipated as this boy, Lance, and yet no one had ever seen him play or even knew if he could play.

"Grass fairies," Pecker said.

"What?" Doc asked him.

"I've never seen a soccer player who was committed to anything else," Pecker said. "He'll probably come out for a practice and then decide to go kick a ball around in a pasture."

Doc shook his head. "If the boy can play first base, I don't care if wears a soccer uniform to our games. These boys need to play all the sports they can."

A minivan rolled up just as the boys were taking the field to loosen up their arms by tossing the ball back and forth across the infield. A sliding door opened, and an athletic-looking tow-headed boy got out of the van and walked toward the field with his parents. Frank went out to meet them. It was a good sign that Lance had a baseball glove, and by the looks of it, a worn one.

Doc couldn't stand the suspense. "Alright, boys, get to your positions. Hoss, third; E-Mar short; C-Dog at second, and Cody get behind the plate. Jordan, get on the pitcher's mound. The rest of you boys head to the outfield with Coach . . . Pecker." The customary chuckles filled the air.

The first base position was glaringly vacant.

Frank extended a hand to Lance's dad and introduced himself. The introductions were cordial.

Frank half turned to the infield and pointed to the open first base position.

"I'm not going to lie to you," Frank said. "You can see that no one is at first base. We don't have a consistent first baseman without shifting boys around and weakening our defense. Lance, we are hoping you can play first base for us."

The boy beamed. He turned to his dad and then back to coach Frank. "I've always played center field because I'm fast."

"Well, I'd like you to run over there to first base and see how it fits for you," Frank said, and the boy took off across the dirt infield to first base. Frank heard Doc introduce himself to the boy and then introduce him to the other boys in the infield.

Frank continued standing with Lance's parents. They started back toward the van, and Frank said, "Wait just a minute, please. Let's watch it together."

Doc hit a hard grounder to third and said, "Hoss, take it to first."

Hoss, a big, sturdy boy, took the ground ball and shifted two steps toward first as he gripped the baseball's seams. Then he uncorked a hard throw right at the new first baseman. The ball was on Lance faster than he expected, but he instinctively got his left foot on the base and received the throw."

"Good throw," he shouted over at the third baseman, who said, "Good catch."

Lance then reached back and threw the ball home to Cody so that Doc could continue hitting infield grounders.

Doc hit one to short and said, "E-Mar, take it to first."

E-Mar, a quiet, fleet-footed athlete, took one step to his right, gloved the grounder, and whipped the ball to first base. As a forecast to his future as an elite college pitcher, the ball curved naturally on its way to first. Lance stayed right with the ball and fielded it at his knees.

"Good throw," he shouted. E-Mar coolly pointed to him as if to say, "Nice job."

Frank turned to face Lance's parents.

"I've coached a lot of boys' baseball," he said. "Lance's soccer days are over for this spring. He's a natural over there. If you commit him to us for the spring, this team will win a championship, and he might even be an All-Star in our division." It was big talk for five minutes into a preseason practice, but Frank knew talent when he saw it.

"You think so?" Lance's mom said. She smiled in shocked surprise.

"I can make that work, but he won't be available on Sundays, so he can play soccer, and when it doesn't conflict with baseball games or practices, I'll let him go to soccer," the boy's dad said.

Frank reached out and shook the man's hand. "Deal."

Later, as all the boys left practice for the day, Doc said, "Frank, do you think Jesus cares if we have a first baseman? We joked about praying for a first baseman, but do you think Jesus cared enough to send one?"

Frank let out a big sigh. "I think Jesus wants us to be content, and right about now, I'm pretty content. The rest of it, we'll just have to ask him when we get to heaven."

⚾ ⚾ ⚾

Richie was a rambunctious little boy who played right field. He often came to practice with an untucked T-shirt that read, "Satan is a poo-poo head." Frank constantly reminded him to tuck in his shirt. Frank was a stickler for shirts tucked into pants and hats worn correctly. Many a boy ran laps around the big Field of Dreams for a hat facing backward.

"If you look sloppy, you will play sloppy," Frank barked loudly again so the parents could hear him while parked at the edge of the outfield. "We won't have sloppy, and we won't have goofy. Both are a disease."

"Except for Coach Pecker," Doc chirped. "He's always goofy."

"Present!" Pecker shouted, and raised his hand.

One spring afternoon at the Field of Dreams, Richie began waving his arms out in right field. He had missed a hit to right field and chased it to the tree line of the woods.

Seeing the boy waving for attention, Doc jogged in his direction, asking if he needed to visit the woods. Frank was pitching in one of the sandlot intra-squad scrimmages he used to close every practice. To avoid the possibility of injury, Frank stopped the scrimmage while Doc visited with Richie, and to Frank's surprise, the two turned and walked slowly toward the tree line of the woods in right field.

All the boys on the team watched them walk away from the field. "Everything okay, Doc?" Frank shouted.

The pair stopped at the tree line and stared at the ground. Frank began jogging in that direction, and when he got to the man and boy, he paused in disbelief.

Before them was the small lifeless body of an animal. It was a pale red with a bushy, long tail and a face that curiously looked more like a cat than a dog.

"It's a fox," Frank said out loud.

Richie stood there. "I saw it when I came to get the ball." With his left hand, Frank pulled the boy away from the animal, ensuring Richie had not and did not touch it.

By now, the entire team had joined the assembly in right field.

"I'll call the Department of Natural Resources tomorrow," Frank said. "We should let them know."

"Let's bury it," one of the boys said. "It deserves a burial."

Frank looked at Doc, who said, "Well, we've prayed for players and given thanks for rainouts. We might as well bury a fox." He took a closer look at the animal. "There's no sign of rabies, but no one should touch it."

Frank went to his truck and removed a shovel. He carried a shovel and a rake at all times – just in case he needed either or both for fieldwork here or at the ballpark's practice fields. He handed the shovel to Pecker.

"Alright, let's finish practice while Coach Willet digs a hole," Frank said. "We'll bury the little fox after practice. I don't want any of you close to it and don't touch it."

"So I'm the team gravedigger now," Pecker said.

Doc patted him on the shoulder. "And if you do a good job, I might be able to get you some other work. We're always looking for gravediggers."

Two things came from the death of the fox that day.

First, the boy named Richie picked up a new nickname, Foxy.

Second, after practice ended, there was a funeral in right field.

Frank put on a pair of old work gloves and gave Doc a second pair. The two men used the rake and shovel to ease the fox into a thirty-nine gallon leaf bag, tied it off, and then put the bag into a second bag. Using the shovel to ease the fox into the grave, Frank covered up the animal. E-Mar took two sticks from the woods and Doc placed them over the grave in a makeshift cross. C-Dog, the second baseman, handed Doc some weeds, and the coach curiously smiled at Frank as he lay them on the grave.

"You want to say something, Coach Frank?" Doc asked.

"I'll pray," Frank said. The boys took off their hats. "Lord, we know that you love everything in creation. You love us, and you loved this little fox and all the other creatures on Earth. We know you watched him and you cared for him, and when it was his time to die, you had us find him so we could care of him too. Help us love one another and love your creation. Amen."

Several of the boys said "Amen," which caused Frank to smile at Doc and shrug his shoulders.

Frank didn't realize what happened when he offered that simple prayer. Baseball players might have heard a coach or two recite the Lord's Prayer from Matthew's Gospel, chapter 6, but they had rarely heard a coach pray out loud – and for a dead animal.

The season opened in late March that year. In the first game, Lance went 4-4, scored three runs, and had five RBIs in a 24-1 thrashing that Doc simply described as "shock and awe."

The Sharks rolled to a 15-1 record, losing only a 3-2 contest on a night in March when the sky spit a cold rain – just above freezing – for most of the game. The Sharks center fielder walked out of the dugout, crying that it was just too cold for him to play anymore; his daddy took him home.

"I can hardly blame him," Frank said when he called the boy's home later that evening. "One day, we grown men will look back on games like this and wonder, 'What the hell were we thinking, asking little boys to play baseball in weather like this?'"

On the season, Lance was the team's second-best hitter, logging a .412 batting average with twelve extra-base hits. He led the team in RBIs with thirty-six and was second in runs scored with twenty-seven. As the team's first baseman, he recorded ninety-four putouts.

After defeating the Eagles 11-3 on a Saturday in mid-May for the division championship, Frank met Lance's excited parents as he exited the third base dugout. He smiled at them, winked, and said, "I told you that if he played, we would win a championship."

"You were right," his dad said. "I thought you were crazy, but you were right."

The crazy part was yet to come.

The Sharks had four players make the division's All-Star team that season: Hoss, E-Mar, Lance, and Jordan. Jordan had led the team in batting average, Hoss far and away led the team in extra-base hits with twenty-one, and E-Mar and Hoss both led the team in runs scored. E-Mar had fifty-two assists and putouts at shortstop.

Frank coached the division's All-Star team because the Sharks were the division champions, and he chose Doc as his assistant. The Eagles' head coach rounded out the coaching staff, but Frank let Pecker help as an unofficial, unrostered practice assistant. Though Little Wood's recreation baseball career was short-lived, Pecker had remained as one of Frank's assistant coaches. Frank didn't have the heart to turn him away, and both he and Doc agreed that Pecker's good-hearted sense of humor was good for the team's chemistry.

The first All-Star tournament was in mid-June. School was out, pools were open, and it was undeniably summer in central South Carolina. The day's heat gave way to afternoon thunderstorms that either left the evenings cool and cloudy or miserably hot and humid. There was no way to know in June; by August, no one cared. In August, it was hellishly hot twenty-four hours a day. Central South Carolina was built on top of hell, and July and August proved it every year. Rumor was that a vent pipe could be opened on most ballparks, and the poor souls could be spied upon as they shoveled coal in hell's furnace.

At a pretournament coaches meeting, Frank stared at a list of teams that had qualified for the All-Star tournament. One team and one coach jumped off the page at him. Ameriland was a growing community about ten miles from Concord. It had pulled together community support with tax dollars to build a first-class recreation complex. It made no qualms about recruiting coaches who may or may not have lived within the playing district's boundaries. While the league required players to prove residency and play within their boundaries, any restrictions on coaches were not necessarily enforced.

Ameriland had recruited Alex Coldstone.

Frank saw Alex's name on the list of teams just when the coach walked into the room. He wore his customary black shorts with a white pressed Polo brand shirt and a black hat with the letter *A* embroidered on the front. Alex had removed his mirrored sunglasses and put them over the top of his hat. He scanned the room, and his eyes met Frank's. He walked over and sat as close to Frank as possible.

"Hello, Alex," Frank said, reaching across a chair to shake the man's hand.

"Frank," Alex said, smiling, shaking hands. "I've got a really good team in this tournament. You aren't going to beat us."

Frank smiled and rolled his eyes before turning back around for the meeting.

Still, Frank wasn't kidding himself. Ameriland was going to be tough competition in this five-team tournament. The winner advanced; the four losers went home.

The Concord All-Stars opened the double-elimination tournament with a 7-4 victory over the Pineview community, and that set up Concord's second-round game against Ameriland.

Frank barely spoke to Alex throughout the game. Concord was up 8-2 before giving up four sixth-inning runs and then barely holding on to an 8-6 win. Following the game, as was customary, the two teams met at midfield to shake hands. Frank looked for Alex but couldn't find him. Someone said he had gone to the restroom.

Frank knew what lay ahead in the third game – it was a team from the Midland community. Frank realized he had overlooked Midland by overfocusing on Ameriland. It was going to be a tough contest – both teams were undefeated. Concord went up 3-0 in the top of the first but then collapsed in an 11-3 loss that sent them to the loser's bracket and the edge of elimination in the double-elimination tournament.

"Thankfully, we have tomorrow off," Frank told his team. "I know you are tired. We play a long, tough season in Concord, and then we breathe deep before another intense All-Star season. My advice to you is to take tomorrow completely off from baseball. Go swimming. Do what you want, but come out in two days ready to play hard."

The parents complained as they limped away from the field – the boys had already forgotten about the big loss. An impromptu post-game party moved from the ballpark to nearby Zesto's restaurant.

⚾ ⚾ ⚾

Midland's win sent Concord to the tournament loser's bracket and a rematch with an all-familiar foe – Ameriland. Before the game, almost as if it were meant to be, Frank arrived at the ballpark just behind Alex Coldstone. Frank intentionally parked beside him, forcing a meeting.

"Alex," Frank said. "I didn't get to shake your hand after our last game." He extended his hand, and Alex took it. "Good luck tonight."

Alex looked at Frank behind his mirrored sunglasses. "Loser goes home and starts their summer," he said.

Frank couldn't help it. "Why did you leave Concord to coach at Ameriland?"

Alex hoisted his team's equipment bag over his left shoulder. "Change of scenery," and then more bluntly, "and better talent on the field." He began walking toward the minor league fields. Frank just watched him go. He waited several minutes so no one would see him walking with Alex or in the coach's shadow either.

Before the start of each game, each team was allowed a few minutes of infield practice. Frank hated hitting pregame balls to his infield, because he wanted them to play perfectly, and boys were rarely ever perfect at anything. So Doc took two baseballs to home plate and hit the balls around the infield, allowing each position player to make two throws to first and another to home. Another coach went to the outfield and tossed long balls to the outfielders. Frank sat in the dugout and watched. As an unofficial coach, Pecker was forced to watch from just behind the dugout.

Doc returned to the dugout with the team. He took the two baseballs used for the infield practice and stuck them inside the top of the dugout fence, near the dugout entrance.

"They look tense," Doc said. "Even our Sharks. I've never seen them look so tense."

"Tell me about it," Frank said. "It was all I could do to sit here and keep my mouth shut while they kicked the ball around during that infield practice."

After five innings, Concord was down 5-0 to Ameriland. Frank was despondent. Doc was exasperated. He had tried everything to coach up the boys, but nothing worked. Concord had put up only two base runners in five innings, and neither had advanced past first base.

Before sending Ben out to lead off the top of the sixth and final inning, Frank pulled his team together on the dugout bench.

"This is it, boys," he said. "We are in a deep hole. It's our last chance."

"Boys," Pecker said as he pressed his face on the back fence of the dugout, "you can't dig your grave, jump in, bury yourself, and then blame it all on the shovel."

Doc began laughing and shaking his head. From that day forward, Doc brought a shovel to every Sharks game and propped it in the corner of the dugout.

Frank said, "Okay, let's go out there and score some runs."

Ben, a lanky left fielder, led off with a single. He advanced when the next hitter fouled out to the catcher. Concord's All-Stars then rolled off seven consecutive singles, spraying the ball all over the outfield, with leadoff hitter Cody driving in the final two runs of a seven-run frame that gave Concord a stunning 7-5 comeback lead. The pressure had dramatically shifted to Ameriland, and they only had three outs to tie or win the game.

The comeback had drawn the entire tournament to the game, and the crowd now swelled four rows deep behind and around home plate. As the Concord fans came to life, the boys did too. New life was breathed into the game.

"This is why I love baseball," Frank said over the noise. He looked at Doc. "It can be a flat as a board for a handful of innings, and then the excitement just takes off."

"Kinda like fishing," Pecker said, hopping up and down in excitement. "I once sat for eight hours on the lake, and then, boom, caught the biggest bass I'd ever seen."

Frank stared at him and then politely said, "Yes, just like that."

Ameriland was not finished. With two outs in the bottom of the sixth, the leadoff hitter reached on an error and scored on a hit by the next batter. The score was tied up 7-7 on another uncharacteristic Concord error, and the inning ended with a guarantee of extra innings.

"Free baseball!" Pecker shouted. "Free baseball for one and all!"

In the top of the seventh, Hoss singled and advanced to third on a passed ball and a fielder's choice. When Grant grounded out to short, Doc sent Hoss steamrolling home from third on the shortstop's throw to first. Concord's big catcher scored to send the team up 8-7 over Ameriland.

Frank looked across the field at the bottom of the seventh to see Alex Coldstone pacing in his dugout. He was not happy, but was too cool to take it out on his players. He said loud enough for everyone to hear, "Let's get two and go home."

The first Ameriland hitter hit a screaming line drive to first base, and Lance – whose bat had been quiet for much of the tournament – stabbed the ball for the first out. He made it look effortless, and Frank shot a look at the boy's dad, who was gladly accepting back slaps from other parents standing near him. It made Frank smile. "Soccer, my ass," Frank thought.

The next hitter singled and recklessly took second base on the throw back to the infield. The tying run was now in scoring position.

"Come on, boys, let's hold them right here," Frank shouted, but his words died under the frenzy created in the crowd behind him. The players could not hear the coaches. An overflow crowd now stretched around the outfield fence.

"Let's just be quiet and let them play, Frank," Doc said. "Remember, they are All-Stars. They know what to do." Frank smiled. He and Doc had always lived by the rule that coaching took place at the Field of Dreams; coaching was rarely effective during the drama and tension of a game.

Ameriland's next hitter had already singled and scored in the game. He hit a line drive to short, and E-Mar ran two steps to his left and snagged it for the second out. Glancing at second, he realized the runner had started for third and was trying to retreat to second. Austin, Concord's second baseman, had slipped in behind the runner and was standing on the base. E-Mar flipped the ball to Austin for the third out, and the game was over. Concord won, 8-7.

The field erupted as the Concord All-Stars poured into the center of the field, with coaches, parents, and fans joining them. No championship was won that day, but the thrill of the comeback was hard to beat.

Doc put his arm around Frank's shoulder. "There's nothing like this ride you and I are on," he said. "These boys will grow up and tell this story to their children." Frank smiled and looked for Alex Coldstone and then saw him coming straight for him. As Alex approached, he took off his black cap and held his sunglasses. He stuck out his hand toward Frank.

"I tip my hat to you, Frank," he said. "You have some kind of lucky charm. I don't ever want to play you again. Good game." Frank shook his hand, and the two men parted.

⚾ ⚾ ⚾

Concord met Midland in the tournament's championship game and lost, 7-0. Some said it was a hangover from the big win over Ameriland. Some said it was just time for baseball to be over for Concord's team. Once the game was over, Frank was ambivalent about it. He was already thinking about the fall instructional league and preparing for the next season.

⚾ ⚾ ⚾

Frank had waited until after the All-Star season to schedule the year-end celebration party for his Sharks team. Several of the team's families had planned early summer vacations. Inclement weather moved the party from outdoors to inside the big Baptist church's gymnasium on Main Street.

"You know, a cheeseburger tastes just as good if it's eaten outside or inside," Pecker said while loading his plate with three of the delicious burgers that Doc had cooked on a grill just barely sheltered from the rain.

"I hope you enjoy every one of those," Doc said, smiling.

After the meal, Frank made sure each player knew of his contributions to the team that year, because every player had something of which he could be proud. Frank knew about every player's successes because he kept the scorebooks.

Frank gave every player a copy of the weekly newsletters he wrote in one-page newspaper style, carrying reports of each game complete with updated player stats and game ball recipients.

Frank even took time to recount the story of the fox.

Following the party, as parents packed up their families, Frank noticed Foxy lingering behind – even as his parents took cleaned-up food containers to their car.

Frank eased away from the cleanup to where Foxy was standing, one foot propped behind him on a red-brick wall. He had chocolate frosting from celebratory cupcakes at the corners of his mouth.

"Is everything okay, Foxy?" he asked.

The boy looked up into the coach's face and then looked at the floor before whispering something that Frank couldn't quite hear.

"You need to look at me and speak up."

Foxy looked up at him, and Frank was moved by the tears welling up in the big blue eyes. Frank immediately dropped into a catcher's squat so that he was eye to eye with the little boy.

"You know how you prayed for the little fox?" Foxy whispered. Then, even softer, he asked, "Will you pray for me?"

Frank grabbed that little boy and pulled into him a tight hug and felt two little arms wrap around his neck.

"I would love to pray for you, Foxy," Frank said. "Is everything okay with you?"

"My papa is sick," he whispered.

Frank was overcome. He had been just a little bit older than Foxy when his beloved grandmother – his Granny – had died from cancer. It had been a shock to Frank's childhood – one it took him a long time to get over. He knew the heartache that this little boy was feeling – he knew it to his core. He felt a knot working its way up into his throat.

Right there, with all the party cleanup clattering around them, Frank Wilcox prayed over his young player, prayed for Foxy's grandfather, prayed for the boy's family, and prayed for the hurt to go away. When he finished praying and released the little boy, he took a napkin and wiped both their eyes. He also wiped Foxy's face and got the chocolate off it.

"You are going to play in the fall league, right?" Frank asked him.

Foxy nodded, sniffling and regaining his composure, that he would play in the fall. "Can I be on your team?"

"Absolutely," Frank said. "You can't play for anyone else this fall or next spring. You and I are stuck together." There was a little smile that crept across the boy's face. Frank turned to see his parents at the door, apparently watching the entire scene.

Once again, from somewhere or maybe just deep within, Frank heard the voice of Terry Thompson, and Frank smiled.

"It's not about baseball; it's about the boys."

⚾ ⚾ ⚾

As the summer waned and the humidity broke in September, Doc suggested inviting some boys to the ballpark for a hit-around and some infield practice. He and Frank made a list of twenty boys they knew, thinking they might even let the boys choose up and play a scrimmage.

When Frank called Lance's number, Frank got a recording, "*This number is no longer in service.*" He double-checked the number and called it again. The message was the same. He drove to Lance's house, and a For Sale sign was stuck in the front yard. A neighbor, mowing the next-door lawn, saw Frank and told him the family had moved to Atlanta. The dad had an unexpected job transfer – a promotion he couldn't turn down.

Doc shook his head at the news.

"I'm telling you, Frank, that boy was an answered prayer," Doc said. "We asked for a first baseman for this one special season, and we got one for this one season. Don't ever tell me God doesn't love baseball."

A decade later, Doc called Frank to tell him the news. He had discovered Lance through a search of social media, and neither he nor Frank was surprised to learn their former first baseman had shined and starred as a premier Atlanta high school athlete . . . playing soccer. The news made both of them laugh.

The little boys cheered when their dad returned with the Dippin' Dots. Whitney took her helmet of ice cream and said to Bradley, "Can you give him some money?"

Before Bradley could reach for his wallet, Frank said, "Nope. This is on me. It's all God's money." He handed the ice cream to the couple behind him and to Phil, and then put the carrying box underneath his seat. He sat down.

Whitney said, "Thank you so much."

"You are so welcome," Frank said. "One day, you and Bradley may bring your children to a Braves game, and I hope you remember to get seventh inning Dippin' Dots."

Another scoreless inning and the natives were getting restless. The Braves still led 2-0, and some fans were starting to pack up for home. After all, Thursday was a workday in the free world.

EIGHTH INNING
SPONGEBOB

G-Double O-D

E-Y-E

Good eye, Good eye, Good eye

"**W**hy are you here by yourself?" Phil asked Frank as they waited at the start of the eighth inning. "Pardon me for asking, but I see you are wearing a wedding ring. You just don't think of folks being by themselves at a baseball game."

Frank held his left hand. "I've battled a little bit of the blues lately; I thought coming to a game by myself might help me shake off this pestilence. I think my wife was glad to have the night off."

The woman behind him patted his shoulder and said, "Well, I'm glad you were able to be here with us."

Frank looked back without really turning and said, "Thank you."

"You keep a pretty good scorebook," the man behind him said, leaning forward to look over Frank's shoulder. "I'll bet you either played baseball or coached it."

"I wasn't much of a player," Frank said. "As a young man, I got involved in coaching boys recreational baseball and ended up doing that for a lot of years."

213

The dad in front of him said, "Do you miss coaching, or are you glad it's over?"

"When I was in the thick of it, I hated the idea of it all coming to an end," Frank said. "I used to look at that twenty-game schedule and dread it ending. But as I got toward my youngest son's final season, my joints all hurt, and I could no longer throw hard enough for the hitters. I gained some weight." He patted his stomach.

"I hear that," the grandfather in front of him said. "Packed on the pounds myself as I got older."

"Toward the end, I went to the bathroom before the start of one game," Frank said. "There were several players from other teams in there. I found an empty stall and was standing there doing my business.

"I heard one player ask another, 'Who are y'all playing today?' and another one answered, 'We are playing the one with the fat coach.'" Frank laughed. "I knew they were talking about me. So I figured it was time to turn off the scoreboard."

"Did you coach your sons?" the dad asked.

"Yes," Frank said. "They were all good players, better than average, I think, but none of them went on to play school ball. I was too hard on them, probably. I think they learned enough to coach their children one day – if their children even want to play."

The grandfather in front looked at his son. "He says I was hard on him too. I told him that you can't get the wood smooth unless you bear down on the sander."

"If my boys had a bad game, they ran to their mama's van to ride home with her," Frank said. "I can't stand sloppy defense or watching a third strike with a man in scoring position."

The dad nodded his head and tapped the two little boys on the head. "See, it's not just me saying that same thing."

"Of all the boys you coached, was there a favorite?" Phil asked. "Besides your own, of course."

"I wouldn't say there was a favorite, but my wife will one day call about a dozen former players to tote my box down to the front of a church," Frank said, laughing. He smiled and thought of Doc, who used to say, "Which of these boys are gonna carry your box, Coach Frank?"

"Don't talk like that," Whitney said. "That's too sad."

"Well, Whitney," Frank said, smiling, "I certainly hope they aren't planning my funeral service tomorrow. I mean, I want to go to heaven, but not necessarily today."

The inning was about to start.

"SpongeBob," Frank said.

One of the little boys in front furrowed his brow and looked at Frank. "SpongeBob?"

"I can't say he was my favorite player, but I can say that I will never forget him," Frank said.

⚾ ⚾ ⚾

Frank was shirtless and stared into his bathroom mirror. The face looking back at him was tired, and he had just gotten a full night's sleep. The morning sun was yet to rise, and Frank leaned on the lavatory and stared into the mirror.

"So this is the squeeze," he said to the man staring back at him. "My daddy warned me about it." He dropped a towel from around his waist and stepped into the hot shower. He closed his eyes as the hot water beat directly on his face.

Tom Wilcox warned Frank that "the squeeze" would come one day as it came for most men. There would be the pressure that came at work, the pressure that came with a growing family at home, and the pressure that came from church and community obligations. Financial, relational, and physical pressure all coming together with deadlines and time constraints. The pressure – the squeeze – from all those directions, all at the same time, would change a man. It had changed Tom Wilcox. During his own squeeze, Tom spent less time with his sons playing around in the yard, worked longer and harder, and seemed angrier most of the time.

"I won't lie, Son," Tom told Frank during his oldest son's junior year of high school. "Sometimes the squeeze gets so bad that I just want to go sit in the woods all by myself for about a week."

Frank was feeling it. He and Vicki now had four sons under the age of thirteen. They both worked in offices that involved a thirty-minute one-way commute. He and Vicki didn't speak until they got to work, then telephoned one another to go over the day's schedule. It seemed one or more of the boys had to be somewhere every evening, and goodness knows there was no time for anyone to be sick and need a doctor's appointment.

Frank was adamant that the boys have a hot meal each night, and while he whipped together a meal, Vicki lorded over homework around the kitchen table. Some nights, dinner and homework merged, and that led into a regimented bath time, which then led to bedtime, a story or two, and a prayer. Frank and Vicki collapsed into the bed, mumbling to one another and looking to start the process all over again the next day.

Adding to the pressure was Frank's employment. He had a good job with the South Carolina Baptists, helping churches with communication and leading the corporate marketing effort in the state, but more and more his work was distracted by the boys and their interests, or doctor's appointments, or meetings at schools. His work suffered, and he knew that others knew, and he could imagine the whispering even if it was just his imagination. One afternoon he fell asleep at his desk, asleep from exhaustion, and missed an important meeting.

The squeeze was real.

"What I make each month is really just going to childcare," Frank told Vicki one morning as he dressed for work. That statement led to a Sunday afternoon of solitary work at the Field of Dreams, where Frank poured out his troubles to the Lord under the shadow of Round Top's steeple. Roxie sensed Frank's pain and faithfully sat beside him at the old picnic table.

In months, Frank was self-employed. He decided to take his marketing acumen – aimed at the faith community – and start his own business from home. Vicki was in full support because Frank now had time flexibility, especially as it came to raising the boys and getting them around town. It was a shift in roles, but Vicki said, "Why not have a daddy who is all in with everything in his boys' lives?"

While the squeeze let up on the home front, starting a new business added to the pressure on the financial front. Immediately, the family's income was cut significantly. Aside from daycare costs, the expenses were largely the same. Frank was scraping along financially as he worked to promote and advertise a consulting practice that would ultimately grow nationally, but was currently in its infancy.

As the Christmas holiday season approached that first year, Frank stared at an empty checking account and wondered how the family would piece together Christmas for the boys. He finally had to surrender it all to the Lord, and the Lord responded. A church called, needing to hire Frank's company for the following spring, but wanted to pay fully in advance from the current budget. That gave Frank the assurance he needed that even during this season of the squeeze, the Lord was going to be faithful.

Frank suggested that it might be easier if he didn't coach baseball, making him more available to help Vicki shuttle all the boys to practices and games. He could be an assistant here and there, but leave the head coaching to someone in less of a squeeze.

"No," she said. "You can quit your job, but you can't quit coaching." They both laughed at how it sounded. "Seriously, honey, you have to coach, because that lets us control one schedule. You can also better work with other coaches on their practice schedules for one or two of the other boys. You can't stop coaching."

Even Frank's coaching brought pressure to this season of his life.

Frank had now coached for almost a decade in Concord. His Sharks had won championships in two of the past four seasons and had won fifty of seventy-five spring games during the same run. He and Doc had created an environment of fun, serious baseball education. They gave away game balls, Frank sent every boy home with a printed team newsletter each Monday, the two men had optional weekend and offseason practices, they bought ice cream, and they worked hard as encouragers.

Because of it, Frank and Doc were sought-after, much-requested coaches. They were also expected to continue winning as if they had mysteriously discovered the golden ticket. As the head coach, Frank felt the pressure – so much that he constantly told Doc and Pecker, "We must love this team more than anyone else loves this team. We can't give anyone any reason to say we aren't fully committed to every player, every practice, and every game."

The night before that season's draft, he was reviewing a spread-sheet of boys making their way up from the younger league. On his desk was a photograph of his first team – that ITT Rayonier team – and Frank stared into every face. He also stared at himself. He was laughing in the photograph. Those were the days before the squeeze. These days, he was no longer laughing.

The squeeze was changing Frank Wilcox. It was going to get worse.

⚾ ⚾ ⚾

The draft that season was at the local high school, and the league was downsizing by two teams. Frank's team merged with another team through a hat draw, and Frank walked outside two hours later with a roster loaded with talent. He had a veteran infield, a strong 1-2 pitching combination, and arguably one of the best catchers in the league, and he had drafted speed in the outfield. What's more, he had Big D.

Big D was a giant of a ten-year-old. Without question, he was the hardest-throwing pitcher in the league and taller than most thir-teen-year-olds. He towered on the mound and at the plate, and his effortless swing could launch a baseball at any time. He could have conjured up images of the Philistine warrior Goliath, roaring at the Israelites in the Valley of Elah, but all those who knew Big D knew he was a special boy. As big and intimidating as he could appear, Big D was equally polite, friendly, respectful, and encouraging. A huge smile lit his face. An ugly, hurtful word never came out of his mouth, and every coach and player regarded him as a wonderful teammate.

"You are a lucky bastard, Frank," one coach said as the coaches left the draft that night. He slapped Frank on the back. "Looks like you will cruise to another championship."

Frank wanted to vomit.

He walked into the house, and Vicki looked up from the homework session.

"How did it go?" she asked.

"Pressure," he said. "I may have one of the best rosters I've ever had. That whole ballpark will expect me to win it all. Don't get me wrong, I like winning, but I feel like we have to win now. It'll look bad on Doc and me if we don't win."

"You mean it will look bad on you," she said. "Don't let all this pressure steal your joy, Frank. Don't turn into another Alex Coldstone. You have a responsibility at the ballpark – a lot of people look up to you." She pointed to four little boys around the table. "These four are always watching you."

Frank knew she was right. He picked up his telephone and began calling his roster, relaying information about the first practice at the Field of Dreams.

It was the new season's first practice at the Field of Dreams; Frank and Doc sat on the Ford pickup's tailgate. Pecker was on the field, organizing the boys into throwing lanes as they arrived for practice. Most boys wore elastic-waisted baseball knickers, the legs pulled down over their socks, and a T-shirt underneath a hoodie. Upon arriving, each boy picked up a baseball from Frank's ball bucket, paired up with another player, and began playing catch with about five yards between them.

"Did you hear the joke about the woman who was about to have a baby?" one boy, nicknamed Ace because of a hat he wore with the number 1 displayed on it, said loud enough for everyone to hear over the steady drumbeat of tossed baseballs. "This lady was about to have a baby, and she goes to the doctor, who says, 'Ma'am, your baby is about to be born, but we've got some bad news for you. You can't pee until that blessed day comes.'"

Laughter filled the air as the boys slowly stopped throwing to listen to the joke.

Ace said, "Listen, listen," he called his teammates to be quiet. "So she goes back to the doctor, and he tells her again that she can't pee until the baby is born. She's going crazy, right? So she goes home and doesn't pee for two weeks."

"Was she drinking anything?" one boy asked.

"Of course," Ace said. "Blue Powerade or girlie stuff, like martinis."

Ace was now laughing as the boys were listening, and one said, "Hurry up, Ace, all this talk about pee has made me need a trip to the woods." Ace nodded his head.

"Okay, finally, she can't hold it any longer, and so she goes back to the doctor," Ace said. "And, just like before, he says, 'I'm sorry, ma'am, just a little longer. You have to hold it for just a little longer.'" Ace paused as he prepared the punch line. Frank and Doc were watching as the baseball had stopped. Frank was already laughing. This kid was a great storyteller.

Ace continued, "She said, 'I just can't do it, Doc,' and he said, 'I'm sorry, ma'am, but you have to hold it just a little longer.' And about that time, the baby stuck his head out and said, 'Hey, Doc, what do you think I am, a submarine?'"

One boy threw his glove at Ace, and Frank shouted, "Alright, warm those arms up." The drumbeat continued.

Doc leaned over and whispered, "I'm surprised no one asked from where the baby stuck his head out?"

"I suspect that will be asked and answered when they are sure we aren't listening," Frank said.

Frank hopped off the tailgate to begin practice when Doc said, "What in the world?"

Walking toward them was an average-sized blond nine-year-old wearing a grin that seemed to stretch from one ear to the other. Unlike the other sloppily dressed boys, this one wore regulation baseball pants with his jersey from the previous year's team perfectly tucked into his waistband. His socks, belt, and hat all matched the jersey.

He stopped in front of Frank and Doc, his smile almost a laugh, and said, "I'm sorry I'm late. It's my fault. It won't happen again." He looked around at the players' bat bags tossed here and there on the ground. He then walked over and, using a spring-snap clip, hooked his bag to the backstop fence, ensuring it was off the ground. As the two coaches watched, he unzipped his bag and took out his glove.

He carefully rezipped the bag. He then turned to see the two coaches again and smiled again.

"Hey!" he said, and with his ungloved hand, held chest high, gave an open-handed wave to the two men – not two feet from him. "You want me to throw some?"

Doc hopped off the back of the truck. "Come on, SpongeBob. I'll throw with you."

Nickelodeon had a television cartoon series about a good-natured, optimistic, hard-working, and, yes, infectious, sea sponge named SpongeBob. The nickname fit this young baseball player to a tee.

⚾ ⚾ ⚾

Right on cue, that season opened horribly.

A crowd gathered for the opener because everyone wanted to see Big D on the mound, throwing BBs to hitters less than half his size. When Frank was forced to pull his starter in a 2-2 tie, the opposition rallied and won 8-3. The dugout was solemn after the game until SpongeBob said, "It's just one game. We will have a better game next time." A few players smiled, but most of them were in shock. The whispers began and spread through the ballpark. By the end of that Saturday, other coaches passed and dodged Frank like he had a death sentence and they didn't know what to say.

Pecker found him that afternoon, sitting beyond right field all by himself.

"Coach Frank," he said, "that was a tough game this morning."

Frank just nodded his head, sarcastically thanking Pecker for the reminder.

About that time, an old dog – probably an escapee from animal control down the road – stopped within three feet of Frank, raised its back leg and peed on a withering shrub. It was appropriate.

The worst was yet to come. In the second game of the season, Frank kept Big D in the game, but the team's offense only generated three hits in a 3-1 loss though Big D struck out half the boys he faced.

At the next practice, Doc told him the honest truth.

"We can't hit, Coach," Doc said. "Without hitting, no one is really afraid of our pitching. They squeeze the plate, work our pitch counts high, take a walk here and there, and ultimately score just enough runs."

Frank snapped at him. "I've been at this longer than you, Doc," Frank said. "I think I know what the hell is happening." He stalked onto the practice field and spent the next ninety minutes relentlessly hitting ground balls to the infield and fly balls to the outfield. No one said a word – not even as they left the field that horrible day. It was the darkest day of Frank's coaching life.

⚾⚾⚾

The Sharks played "afraid to lose" in the third game, fought off a comeback, and barely won, 6-5. That set up an embarrassing 10-5 loss that dropped the Sharks to a 1-3 start to the season.

SpongeBob's parents had brought the postgame snack, juice packets and a candy bar, and SpongeBob was at the dugout entrance handing out the snack with a cheerful salutation.

"Good game, Hoss," he said to the team's weary catcher.

Big D exchanged a hand slap before taking his snack.

Each boy got a "good game" or "get 'em next time" from SpongeBob as they exited the dugout following the loss. Frank was the last, and SpongeBob handed him a Snickers.

"Would you like a snack, Coach?" he asked.

"Thank you, Sponge," Frank said, taking the candy bar and saying nothing else.

Doc noticed how despondent Frank was to the boy and stepped up to say, "SpongeBob, the snacks today are especially fantastic. You played well out there in the outfield. We are going to be okay."

Frank was already separated from the crowd and making the lonesome loser's walk to the parking lot.

⚾ ⚾ ⚾

Frank did not sleep that night. The squeeze was suffocating. It wasn't just the pressure at home and from starting the new business. He knew that when parents lost respect for a coach's decision-making, the season was lost. There was no getting the respect back. He had watched it happen to even the best of coaches. Despite what they said about it being "just a game" and "it's not all about winning," Frank knew that everyone wanted to win when the scoreboard came on. Community, church, and neighborhood pride was on the line, and Frank knew it. Parents did not want the pity of their friends whose boy was on a winning team, and nothing was worse than being on a losing team that was supposed to be a championship-caliber team.

He stared at the dark ceiling.

⚾ ⚾ ⚾

At the next practice, everyone approached the truck's tailgate in silence. Frank gathered them around the tailgate and stared into their faces. He could tell they weren't sure how he was going to react. None of them looked up at him; they expected him to bring the thunder.

SpongeBob raised his hand from the front row. Frank ignored him.

"Boys, I'm not going to sugarcoat it. We aren't together as a team," Frank said, noticing that SpongeBob still had his hand raised and was smiling. He continued ignoring him. "A lot of you are waiting on Big D to do all the work and win games by himself. That won't happen. He's just one player." Frank looked down, sighed, and said, "Sponge, what is it? You can wait to visit the dang woods."

"We'll win the next one, Coach," the boy said, smiling through big eyes that were overflowing with honesty and genuine optimism. "I believe in you."

Behind those sunglasses, Frank's eyes filled with tears. He bit the corner of his lip and just sat there. He felt his throat tighten. Suddenly, he saw these boys for who they really were – little boys.

Big D was down on one knee and said, "I do, too, Coach. I believe in you."

One or two others, leaders on the team, said, "Let's win this thing, Coach. We can do it."

Another one said, "I'm your son. You know I believe in you, Dad." Frank laughed and wiped his eyes from behind the glasses.

Doc put a hand on Frank's shoulder and squeezed it.

226

It was then and there that Frank came to a hard reality. These boys weren't looking to Big D or a veteran infield to win for them – they were looking to Frank as the head coach. They were trusting him to figure things out and tell them what to do. And Frank was so consumed with stress away from and at the ballpark that he was failing them.

Those words: "It's not about the baseball; it's about the boys."

The team meeting was over. Frank sent them to warm up, and SpongeBob pounded his glove with excitement as he took the field to loosen his arm.

⚾ ⚾ ⚾

The team rallied after that, and though SpongeBob was generally a bench player, more than once he sparked the team at just the right time.

In a game against the Ravens, SpongeBob worked the count to full and then drew a walk. The leadoff hitter singled to right, and SpongeBob – not the swiftest of runners – ran through Frank's sign to stop at second and barreled toward third base. The right fielder came up with the ball, saw the runner going to third, and uncorked a throw across the field.

Pecker shouted from the dugout, "Sponge, you better hurry. Get that piano off your back!"

The ball bounced once on its way to third, and the third baseman caught it. Expecting SpongeBob to slide, the third baseman went to the ground with his glove, ready to make the tag for the second out.

"Go back!" Frank shouted, but SpongeBob either didn't hear him or ignored him. Seeing the third baseman put his glove on the ground to tag him, SpongeBob did the unexpected. He gave a little hop and then gave an awkward kind of slip and then . . .

. . . he jumped over the third baseman.

Frank had stepped close to the base to watch the tag, knowing sometimes he could influence an umpire by yelling, "Safe!" when a play was close. Frank was more surprised than anyone when SpongeBob left the ground, jumped the third baseman, and almost landed on his coach. As Frank staggered backward and fell to the ground, SpongeBob landed just beyond third base and then dove back for it before the bewildered third baseman knew what had happened.

The umpire shouted, "Safe!" and then looked at Frank and said, "I've never seen that one before." Frank sat there, staring at his wide-eyed player as the crowd behind him cheered.

"How did you like that, Coach?" SpongeBob said, breathlessly smiling from ear to ear.

"Don't ever do it again," Frank said, laughing as he stood up and turned to the boy's parents while shaking his head.

The Sharks rolled off four runs in that frame and led 7-5 going to the bottom of the last inning. The Ravens tied the game. In the eighth inning, back to the top of its order, the Sharks scored four runs and held on to win 11-7. SpongeBob walked that last inning and scored on a fly ball sacrifice. His run proved to be the winning run of the game. Though the team's first baseman went 4-4 and the third baseman went 2-3, together totaling six RBIs, Frank gave the game ball to SpongeBob.

No boy, the coach figured, valued it more.

⚾ ⚾ ⚾

In a late-season game against the Blue Jays, Frank arrived at the ballpark to learn his pitcher for the day had the stomach flu. Frank had already pitched Big D that week and could not risk any of his other infielders on the mound.

Huddled with Doc and Pecker around the pregame batting cages, Doc said, "I think Sponge could throw strikes for us. Even if they hit him, we can make the plays."

Frank wasn't sure, but he didn't have many options.

"Sponge, come here for a minute," Doc said.

"What's up?" the boy said, smiling as he walked up to the three coaches.

"Sponge," Frank said, "we have no pitching. I've got to leave Hoss behind the plate. Do you know what that means?"

"We're in trouble," SpongeBob said. Then, he said, smiling, "It's just a game. We'll be fine."

"Sponge," Doc said. "Son, you are going to pitch."

Frank wasn't sure how the boy would take it, but he rolled his eyes and grinned big. "Bring it on," he said confidently. "I can do it."

"You think you can?" Frank said. "You've not pitched before."

"Coach," he said, "I know I can!"

Frank started SpongeBob on the mound. After striking out the leadoff hitter, he then walked the bases loaded.

"Well, we tried," Doc said. He patted Frank on the back. "I hate baseball. It's a cruel game."

Frank shouted, "Time out, Mr. Ump," and walked out of the dugout. As he approached SpongeBob, he held out his right hand,

and Sponge, believing the coach was taking him out of the game, handed him the baseball.

Frank gave the baseball back to his pitcher and continued to hold out his right hand.

"Spit out the gum," Frank said, holding his open hand out. "I didn't come to take you out; I came to get that dang bubble gum." SpongeBob smiled. "You're more worried about chewing that gum than you are concentrating on the mitt."

"Sorry," he said, and spat the wad of Double Bubble into his coach's hand. Frank walked back to the dugout and shook the gum into the trash can. SpongeBob struck out the next two hitters he faced, and in two innings of work, struck out six hitters on the way to victory.

⚾ ⚾ ⚾

Despite their poor start to the season, the Sharks managed to tie the Ravens for the division lead, forcing a best of three series to determine the season's division champ.

The playoff's first game went ten innings before the Ravens scored the decisive run and won the game, 4-3. Frank knew that losing the first game in a best of three was almost impossible to overcome. Losing the game in extra innings meant he had burned half of his pitching with at least two games left to play and had no time to rest Big D.

In the second game, the Sharks jumped to a 4-0 lead in the first inning. Everyone on the field could hear SpongeBob's chatter, whether it was "Down and ready, boys!" or "Strike him out!" He was a constant beacon of encouragement.

That's why what happened next was so painful.

The Ravens rallied, and in the top of the sixth and final inning took a 6-5 lead. The go-ahead run scored on a ball hit to left field, where SpongeBob was playing. Groans lifted from the stands, and Frank felt heartache when the fly ball got past SpongeBob, rolled to the fence, and allowed the Ravens to take the lead. When the next hitter struck out to end the half inning, Doc whispered, "Go meet him as he walks in."

Frank had already started out of the dugout, but then stopped and watched. The team's shortstop and third baseman were already jogging to left field, meeting SpongeBob as he jogged toward the dugout.

As the trio got closer to the dugout, Big D stepped out to meet them. "Hey, Sponge," the big boy said, "we're going to win this right now."

"Let's win this one for Sponge," Hoss said, taking off his shin guards in the dugout. "Let's win this thing and force a game three."

In the bottom of the sixth, the Sharks got two men on base and were still down one run with one out. Big D came to the plate and, on the first pitch, drove a ball over the left field fence and into the parking lot for a three-run walk-off home run. The 8-6 victory ensured the Sharks a final one-game playoff against the Ravens – this time with the championship completely on the line.

Big D got the game ball to no one's surprise, but then rolling it around in his hand, he said, "No, Coach. I want SpongeBob to have it. We got to the playoffs because of his attitude." He pitched the ball to Sponge, who smiled a little out of excitement and a little out of embarrassment.

⚾ ⚾ ⚾

The Sharks lost the third and final playoff game but still finished as the division's runners-up with a 13-8 record. At the team party, SpongeBob cried and Frank cried, and most everyone cried.

For Frank, it had not been an easy season on or off the field, but he felt the squeeze was easing up as his family settled into a new routine.

At the end of the party, SpongeBob approached Frank and said, "Thank you for letting me pitch, Coach Frank."

"Sponge," Frank said, "you were fantastic out there. I promise you will pitch more next year."

The little boy smiled and said, "I can't wait. Next year, we'll win it all."

Frank hugged him. "Let's not put any pressure on ourselves."

⚾ ⚾ ⚾

In thinking about SpongeBob's two seasons on the team, Frank had excitedly told his little Turner Field baseball community about taking the gum away from SpongeBob.

"It sounds like you have some very fond memories of coaching," the older lady behind him said. "What became of SpongeBob?"

"He works around state government," Frank said. "He's not a politician, and I'm glad. I'm afraid the dirty world of politics would dim the bright light of one of the best men I know."

"Does he remember when you took the gum from him?" one of the boys in front of Frank asked.

"He does," Frank said. "He was a great teammate because he was always expecting us to win and always encouraging everyone around him. You boys need to be ballplayers like that. Sometimes when you are confident, you play better than you really should."

Whitney said, "I'll bet you hated to see SpongeBob leave your team."

"I did, but he was a perfect player for a perfect time," Frank said. "As he got older, he became a really good baseball player, and I think he played up until he went to college."

After the Braves pulled Smoltz, the pitcher, with one out in the eighth, the Marlins went on to score three runs and take a 3-2 lead into the ninth inning.

"You think the Braves can win it in the ninth?" Phil asked Frank.

The lady behind them said out loud, "SpongeBob would say, 'Absolutely!'" Everyone laughed.

NINTH INNING
UNDEFEATED

The roof, the roof
The roof is on fire
We don't need no water
Let the flames grow higher

F rank stood and stretched at the start of the ninth inning, and he also yawned. It was almost 10:00 p.m., and it was going to be a long, lonely, sleepy drive back to Concord, South Carolina, once this game was over. He smiled at the couple behind him as he turned and sat back down. The crowd was tired and excited all around him, expecting a Braves comeback and dreading the workday ahead.

On behalf of everyone, Phil said, "So, Frank, which team was the best you coached?"

"My last season with Doc, my assistant coach," Frank said. "We were undefeated. 20-0. I coached a few years after that, but the undefeated team was by far the most talented."

"Wow," Phil said. "I guess that *was* your best team." Phil didn't wait on Frank's response. He turned to his right and began talking about a business lunch the next day.

The dad in front of him said, "You must have had a great draft leading up to that season."

"It was a three-year plan," Frank said. "But the season came down to luck – being in the right place at the right time."

The older man in front leaned his head back and said, "That's the truth with just about everything." Frank could not disagree with him.

Bradley, who had sat silent for three hours, now leaned toward Frank and said, "I'd rather be lucky than good."

"You are the luckiest bastard I know," Frank thought, smiling at him and then at Whitney.

As the Braves took the infield for the Marlins top of the ninth, Frank's mind drifted to that special year when Doc's plan met Frank's good fortune, leading to an undefeated season.

⚾ ⚾ ⚾

It was late January and bitter cold in South Carolina. The sun was still setting before six, and Frank turned into the Applebee's parking lot. He wasn't a big fan of Applebee's, but when he and Doc first began having these preseason dinners, it was the only place of its kind. Now, there were a handful of other restaurants just like Applebee's, but baseball superstition forced the two coaches to a high-top table just off the left side of the bar. Pecker was already there with Doc when Frank walked into the "Neighborhood Grill & Bar."

Doc had a glass of sweet tea in his hand, and Pecker was drinking Bud Lite on tap. Frank sat down at the only available seat, and Doc slid a glass of iced water in front of him.

"I knew that's what you would drink," Doc said.

"Damn waste of beverage," Pecker said. "It's dollar beer night, and I'm with two old men drinking sweet tea and water."

Doc had his predictable spiral-bound notebook and had already turned to a page near the back. The funeral director took notes in books like these for every occasion, and his preseason baseball notebook was a navy-blue one. He had written many names on the page, and by the ones with good parents, he had placed a checkmark. If he knew the parents, he had turned the check into an *X*.

"Can we at least order before we have this predraft meeting?" Frank asked. "I'm starving."

"Frank," Doc said, pausing like he always did. "The way I see it, I've got no more than three years left in the tank. I still love baseball and, certainly, the boys, but honestly, there are things I want to do with Miss Allison before we're too old to do them."

"Like what?" Frank asked, recoiling. "And don't get kinky. We can't talk that way in front of Pecker here. Things might get out of hand." He laughed out loud.

"Water boy, don't insult me," Pecker said.

"Well, I want to travel some, especially in the spring and fall, and she has gently reminded me that you and I are always at a ballpark during those times of the year," he said.

Kidding aside, Frank nodded that he understood. He knew the writing was on the wall for himself too. Every joint in his right arm – shoulder, elbow, and wrist – ached almost all the time. He had been to physical therapy for his throwing elbow every summer for the past three years. Standing for long periods also caused his back to hurt, especially the next day.

"I'm not sure I want to do this without you, Doc," Frank said. "You've put up with me all these years, and . . ."

"And it's been a challenge," Doc said, smiling. "Sometimes, Frank, it's been a big challenge. That one two-hour practice, when you blistered that infield with hard ground balls, well, I thought I might have to get therapy for you or insist you come pick out a casket. You weren't doing well."

"I can't stand sloppy defense," Frank said.

"Still, I bet some of those boys have nightmares about it," Doc said, smiling.

"I have nightmares about it," Pecker said. "Let's not kid ourselves. On occasion, we've seen the beast awaken over the past few years."

Frank shrugged his shoulders. "Is this about me or the draft?" he asked.

The three men ordered from an Applebee's waitress. Even though the smothered chicken was no longer on the menu, Frank ordered it, and the kitchen staff creatively made it for him. Doc always ordered a cheeseburger with the cheese on the side. He liked his cheese unmelted. Pecker had a ribeye dinner.

"Just for fun, let's say it's our last three years," Doc said. "Frank, I'd like to suggest something to you. I'd like to suggest that we don't play for this coming year or even the next – we build toward two years from now. Let's see if we can go undefeated, win the division, and have one last time coaching the division All-Star team."

Frank had never coached any other way but for the season at hand and with one lazy eye on the next season. That's how smart coaches drafted. He had never considered building a team for two seasons away.

"I know you already have a plan," Frank said. "What are you thinking?"

Doc smiled gently, in the same gentle way he approached a bereaved family. Outside and away from the funeral home, it was downright creepy.

"This year's draft," Doc said. "There are always a couple of eight-year-olds coming up a year early – usually All-Stars whose parents want them around better competition. You can draft the eight-year-olds with the general understanding that you have them for three seasons."

"Oh no," Pecker said. "That'll hurt us bad this year."

"We're not playing for this year, Pecker," Doc said. "Remember that." He turned back to Frank. "But, yes, we'll probably finish poorly this year, meaning in next year's draft, you'll have a high first-round pick. Next year, you try to get another three – maybe four – All-Stars, and you have them for two years. Follow me?"

Frank was starting to see it.

"Two seasons from now, we'll be sitting there with six possible All-Stars before you even go to the draft," Doc said. "If you want to get greedy in that last year, you take ten-year-olds because you won't be worried about coming back the following year. We'll be loaded, Frank. For that third season, we'll have the most talented team we've ever had. It's reasonable that we could have an All-Star-caliber player at seven of nine positions on the field."

"But, Doc," Frank said, "taking two eight-year-olds this year, we might not win five games, and that will make for a long season."

"But, Frank," Doc said, "we might win more than thirty over the last two years. It seems like a small sacrifice. Plus, we are tipped toward a veteran team this year. It's the perfect year to go young in the draft."

Frank agreed to think about it. On the one hand, he liked the idea of finishing this coaching run with a great team. On the other hand, he still enjoyed coaching from the bottom up – seeing the boys blossom from one year to the next. Frank wasn't sure that would happen if he had a group of superstars. He also hated those preseason expectations of greatness that were sure to come. Doc anticipated what he was thinking.

"Listen," Doc said, patting the tabletop three times with his left hand, "I know what you're thinking. There will still be boys who need Coach Frank to meet them on Saturday mornings and teach them how to throw a baseball while their dads talk business on a telephone." Frank smiled. "You can still coach and teach in fall ball when the scoreboard is turned off."

"I'm in," Pecker said, raising his plastic beer stein. "I'm one double *O* percent all in."

⚾⚾⚾

KJ was a quiet, serious, clean-cut eight-year-old who could have played All-Stars at the younger level but chose not to do so. KJ could play anywhere on the field, and he never lost his cool. When his parents decided to bump him up to the older league a year early, he automatically went to Frank's team because his older brother was already on the Shark's roster.

Killer was KJ's best friend, and the eight-year-old had a cool disposition. He was a lefty who came with speed and athleticism. As an

All-Star in the younger league, Killer had proven versatility in the field and at the plate. He also hit left-handed and provided speed on the bases. Doc's plan included getting Killer, but not in the first round of the draft. Taking an eight-year-old in the draft's first round would be unwise.

"Remember, no one in the draft is thinking like we are," Doc said. "They are looking at the traditional nine- and ten-year-olds; they aren't looking at eight-year-olds. They aren't building for two years away. Most of those coaches will graduate with their son to the older league."

It went just as Doc predicted. When Frank picked Killer in the second round and then was able to get KJ in the fifth, one veteran coach shouted across the draft table, "We're all being played by Frank Wilcox."

"Frank Wilcox, hell," another coach said. "We're being played by that damn undertaker Frank hangs out with." As Frank stared at him, the coach shook his head and mouthed the words, "I know what you are doing." Frank smiled.

Frank completed the draft and felt great about it. In the first round, he had taken Big Jake, a tall, athletic right-handed pitcher who could hit well too. He had gotten two solid infielders, one nick-named Doc, which pleased the damn undertaker, and another wiry speedster nicknamed Noodle. The remainder of the draft featured good ballplayers who could hit and play defense. To that mix, eight-year-olds KJ and Killer fit right in.

Right on cue, one of Frank's late draft picks quit before the first practice. The boy's dad decided to through-hike the Appalachian Trail, and the mom just didn't think she could manage all the practices and games by herself. Frank offered to introduce her to other families living near her, including families that might help the family even beyond baseball transportation. But she declined the help.

As was customary, Frank notified the league of a roster opening and was assigned the next late registrant on the list – a boy nicknamed Vegas for no other reason than Doc overheard him talking about wanting to go there. Giving out all these nicknames had become a big part of playing for Coach Frank, and Frank realized the boys liked to have one. So almost everyone got a nickname – like a fraternity.

Vegas, a pleasant, hard-working boy, had never played baseball before.

"There's your project, Coach," Doc said. "Go work your magic between this year and next."

That season, the Sharks finished 7-10 and were never in contention for the division championship. Every time Frank wanted to get upset about losing – and often losing big – Doc whispered in his ear. "Two years, Frank," he said. "Wait until you see what happens in two years. It's coming. I promise it is."

⚾ ⚾ ⚾

Since the first year he coached in Jenson, Frank had finished off each season with a year-end party, usually a cookout with all the parents bringing sides dishes of baked beans, potato salad, fresh fruit, and brownies. Frank ensured one family always brought brownies. After supper, Frank gave out trophies and certificates and plaques and made sure every boy felt honored and special.

Every boy deserved recognition. Frank had the complete scorebook for every game. He knew there was a moment – in at least one game – when every boy contributed. He was determined to celebrate it.

And no one could stop him.

That year, thunderstorms forced a last-minute relocation of the team party.

"We can have it at the funeral home," Doc said when the only other option seemed to be Joe-Mama's Cadillac Bar & Grill. Frank was against Doc's suggestion at first, but then thought how funny it would be. He relented. That's how the Sharks team party came to be inside viewing room A of the local funeral home in Concord, South Carolina.

As a special treat, Doc gave the team a tour of the casket showroom, which he thought would lead to questions about death, allowing him to ease some of the fear about it. Instead, all the questions focused on Dracula, what kind of casket Dracula used, and if Doc had ever seen Dracula come out of a casket.

"If he's gonna show us the embalming room next, I ain't going," Pecker whispered to Frank. "I didn't sign up for an end-of-year trip to a haunted house with a cheeseburger on the side."

Frank got tickled by the entire scene. As the party closed, he gave each of the boys a fresh copy of the season's weekly newsletters and a big pack of plain M&Ms.

The following January, Frank walked into Applebee's, and Doc already had his notebook opened. Frank sat down, and within minutes his iced water was in front of him.

He tapped his index finger on Doc's notebook. "One day, Doc, we are going to look back on this and see it all as really creepy. Two grown men sitting in an Applebee's talking about boys' baseball like our next meal depends on it."

Pecker came walking up last and pulled out a chair. "Sorry I'm late. Little Wood ran over the neighbor's dog on accident. It didn't kill Old Lucky, thank the Lord, but it's going to cost me a lot of money to keep him alive."

"The dog's name is Old Lucky?" Frank asked.

"Yep. Old Lucky's been bit by at least two rattlers, shot once by a blind deer hunter, and locked in a meat freezer," Pecker said. "Now, he's been run over. That dog will be the last one standing on the planet. Everybody will be gone, and the Lord will say, 'Oh wait, come on, Old Lucky, let's turn out the lights on this big round party.'"

Doc shook his head and shrugged his shoulders, and then he looked at Frank, who simply stared at Pecker.

"Old Lucky?" Frank asked.

Doc tapped the table. "Frank, listen, you and I did not create this little baseball system. We are just operating within the system, not making a dime off anyone, sacrificing our time, and trying to create a meaningful experience for boys and their families around the world's greatest game and pastime. One day, all the boys who play for us will be able – if they want to do it – to go outside and have a game of catch with their boys and girls, and even their grandchildren. Somewhere, they will have an old dusty trophy, and they can say, 'I got this when I played for Coach Frank and his wonderful, personable, and good-looking assistant, Doc Holladay.'"

Frank smirked, and Doc began pouring over his scouting list.

⚾ ⚾ ⚾

In year two of Doc's three-year plan, Frank's first draft pick was a rising All-Star known as Snooky. The boy had gotten the name from a restaurant that his daddy ate at while single and working in a college town. Snooky was a little taller than most of the boys and wiry. He had three older brothers, all of whom had or were playing baseball, and so he had better fundamentals than many boys. He could field and throw and hit, and Doc had already pinpointed him as a possible catcher for the highly anticipated third season. Frank loved the boy's arm action when he threw. It was over-the-top and fluid and came with zip. Frank loved good fundamentals.

"You see the way this boy throws a baseball?" Frank asked Doc one afternoon at practice. "You can tell he's been practicing at home with his brothers, who have good fundamentals. Boys gotta learn, and they learn by mimicking what they get at home. Some of these boys have horrible mechanics, and then you see their dads and understand why. Sometimes I think we should get dads and moms out here and teach them to throw."

Doc had tried to steer Frank toward a hefty, outgoing kid in the draft's second round because, he said, "KJ, Killer, and Snooky all look at me like surgeons, and I'm about to be their patient. I've never seen three more serious boys in all my life."

Pecker said, "Killer kinda scares me. That kid is intense."

Frank didn't hear either of them. He spotted a minute little boy with shaggy hair down over his ears during the player assessment. When the boy hit the ball and started for first, he didn't run there – he flew there. It was such a demonstration of God-given acceleration and speed that Pecker whispered, "Coach Frank, look at the jets on that boy. You can't coach that kind of speed." Frank took him in the second round. His nickname for the next two years – Jet. He, too, had been an All-Star in the younger league.

Rounding out the draft, Frank again drafted for speed – a long, lanky boy nicknamed Stretch – and another whose dad had played on a Little League championship team as a boy.

Following the draft, Doc and Pecker were waiting on Frank in the parking lot. The windy air was cold, and yet Doc was standing out in it. He showed no signs of chill.

"That was a great draft," Doc said excitedly. "Alongside Big Jake, Doc, Noodle, Vegas – it's going to be a great year. I can feel it. We might even win the division."

⚾ ⚾ ⚾

At the season's first practice, the boys assembled around the Ford's tailgate. Frank welcomed them to the team and then handed them a sheet of paper. On the paper, he had typed ten team maxims – a list of fundamental team principles. Some, like "3 and 0, don't you go," related to baseball's unwritten rule not to swing if you had three balls and no strikes while at the plate. Other maxims focused on character, like "Encourage others," and still others focused on avoiding Frank's temper at practice – "Don't be goofy." One maxim always implored the defense to be "Down and Ready" or "Fly Ball – First Step Back."

"Do you still give out baseball cards?" one of the boys asked. Frank's reputation for Monday prizes after practice was now well-known. On Mondays, Frank rewarded players with packs of baseball cards, rubber sharks, money for fly balls caught in the outfield, and M&Ms. Everybody got something because everybody on the team was important.

Frank then noticed a disheveled man, perhaps someone's dad, standing just outside listening range. The man stood with his arms folded, and following the team meeting, as the boys dispersed to warm up, he approached Frank, Doc, and Pecker at the tailgate.

"I want you to know that my son is one of the best you will have on the team," he said, and right away, Frank knew the man was drinking. Frank had grown up around alcoholics and had even attended Alcoholics Anonymous meetings with his paternal grandfather, R. C. Wilcox. Before the dad could say another word, Frank held up his hand.

"You can't come around here if you are drinking," Frank said. "I won't have it."

The man recoiled and then took a cigarette from his front pocket.

"Nope," Frank said. "You aren't going to smoke either. I'm not going to have drinking or smoking around these boys, and especially not on this church's property."

The man stepped in with a snarl. "I don't know that you can stop me if I want to light up, Coach."

Frank said, "I might not be able to stop you, but I bet Roxie can." He pointed to Roxie, who lay near Frank's truck at the line of woods where she always lay during practice. At the sound of her name, the old rottweiler perked up and stood. She might have only been stretching, but she took two steps toward Frank.

The man coughed once or twice and then started toward left field, where his truck was parked.

It was the only time Frank ever had that kind of problem with a parent, and the problem was over as soon as it started.

⚾ ⚾ ⚾

The Sharks opened the season with a 7-6 nail-biting win, coming back from an early 4-2 deficit, and after the sixth game of the season, they were sitting at 5-1. In April, two more wins improved the team's record to 7-1, and Doc excitedly pointed out that his "evil plan" was working – the younger players were showing up as leaders in every category – offense, defense, and pitching. Killer had been the winning pitcher in five of the seven wins.

Needing a win in the last game of the first half to secure a playoff matchup with the Lions, the Sharks stumbled and lost 5-2. The Lions led the division at 8-1, and the Sharks were just behind them at 7-2.

"We're going to be hunted sharks in the second half," Pecker said at a late April practice at the Field of Dreams. "We are going to see every team's best pitcher, especially if they have a second, weaker opponent in the same week." The shark hunt was on.

Opening the back half of the season, the Sharks suffered a 5-3 loss despite playing stellar defensive baseball. Big Jake threw the entire game and only gave up five hits – none of them consecutive. The opponent had scored four runs, plating hitters who got on base by walks.

"Win some, lose some," Frank told his team leader and its All-Star pitcher. "You threw a great game overall, Jake, and now we look to the next one."

The Sharks won their next game, 2-1 in extra innings. When Jet beat out a routine grounder to shortstop, scoring a teammate for the go-ahead run, Pecker slapped Frank hard on the back and whispered, "Speed kills, doesn't it?" Big Jake sealed the win by striking out all three hitters he faced in the final inning.

By the middle of May, the Sharks were 11-5 and slipping out of the playoff conversation. A winning season was guaranteed on May 15, when Big Jake struck out ten of twenty-four hitters that he faced and gave up only three runs. He was also 3-3 at the plate that day.

The Sharks narrowly lost a 7-6 thriller to the Lions before winning the season finale, 13-0. The Sharks finished 13-7, flipping their record from the previous year's 7-10 finish.

⚾ ⚾ ⚾

Despite having lots of All-Star talent on the year's team, Frank paused at the team's year-end party to recognize Vegas, the left fielder with no experience, who had joined the team the previous year only after a drafted player had quit.

"In all my years of coaching, I've never had a player who improved like this one between his first and second years," Frank said, staring into the faces of players and parents, and even a few grandparents. "To get the full picture, you have to look at his statistics from last year. He only scored four runs all year and appeared in no other statistic leaderboards."

Frank had to take a deep breath before finishing. He could feel emotion creeping into his voice. With all the emphasis on winning, nothing gave him more pride than seeing a player blossom and leave his beloved Sharks a more skilled player than when he arrived.

"This year, Vegas led our team in hitting – batting average, number of hits, on-base percentage, and slugging percentage," Frank said. "He led the team in runs batted in and scoring. His fielding percentage was error-free." The coach stared at the shy boy's face and said, "Vegas, you are our most valuable player this year."

Those at the party applauded, and Frank wiped tears from his own eyes. He had a special plaque to give the boy – so rare was his worst-to-first accomplishment. As he put an arm around Vegas and handed him the plaque, Frank said, "Obviously, Vegas deserves to be an All-Star from our team this year, but he is choosing to go with his family on vacation instead, and honestly, I think that makes him even more of an All-Star."

The applause continued as Vegas turned shades of red from all the attention. After the party, all the players and parents congratulated the boy who anchored left field during the entire season, never whining about playing anywhere else.

As the party broke up and everyone left for the summer, Frank called his returning players together for one last word.

"Next year," he said, "next year is going to be special." The six boys stared back at him.

"They are the most serious boys I've ever seen, coach," Pecker said.

"I think they just want to get on to their summer," Frank said.

Coach D. D. Brothers was a former high school baseball coach who now owned a baseball school of sorts. His Baseball Dreams hitting instruction occurred in a small metal building equipped with three batting cages. Players, mostly younger, signed up for hour-long sessions that included muscle memory drills and live hitting off a pitching machine. The coach's sons helped by throwing batting practice in exchange for after-work trips to Outback Steakhouse. In addition to hitting instruction, Coach Brothers also kept an eye open for players with pitching potential and used the last of each session to help boys throw better.

Each of Frank's sons had spent off-season time at Baseball Dreams, and Frank knew that each of his sons had improved at the plate by getting the indoor help with their hitting. Frank especially liked that Coach Brothers was honest in his evaluation and did not overinflate a boy's potential just to string along parents with money to burn on lessons.

Frank also encouraged players on his team to visit Baseball Dreams in the offseason, and he listened when Coach Brothers relayed what Frank should work on when his team regathered for the next season.

The Sharks had certainly benefitted from Doc's three-year strategic plan, but the final piece of the puzzle came through a chance meeting at Baseball Dreams. It was there that Frank was first introduced to Big Mac and the boy's dad, Charlie.

It was the off-season after the Sharks finished 13-7. Frank took his youngest son to Baseball Dreams for a session of hitting and pitching instruction and decided to wait rather than run errands during the hour.

While waiting, Frank met Charlie, whose son Mac was participating in a session simultaneously. Frank studied the boy – a tall, big lefty who stood head and shoulders above all the other boys his age. Frank had been around Concord baseball for a long time and had never seen this boy or met his dad. He assumed Mac was in an older league and was shocked down to his shoes to learn the boy was only ten and could play in the minor league, where Frank coached. Mac, as Frank learned, had previously played in the neighboring Midland league rather than Concord.

"I would sure like to have him on my team," Frank said. "We are going to be pretty darn good anyway, but he would be a valuable addition."

Charlie laughed to himself and then seriously said, "Maybe you can pick him up in the draft. We are transferring this season to play ball at Concord."

Frank turned and collapsed against a wall before sitting down in an old metal chair.

⚾⚾⚾

Because his team had done well the previous year, Frank knew he would have a late first-round draft pick. He also knew Big Mac would stand out at the annual predraft player assessment – a simple skills test for all incoming players to the league. At the player assessment,

Frank knew there was no way to hide Big Mac. He would stand out, and every coach would rank him as a possible first-round pick.

Frank also knew that many coaches took first rounders that they knew well, had previously coached, had been All-Stars in Concord the previous season, or were family friends through neighborhoods and churches. Some were also looking for a pick who came with a dad who could be an assistant coach. Big Mac fit none of those because he was coming from the Midland league.

The draft that year was in the fellowship hall of the big Baptist church on Main Street. Twenty-two coaches were sitting around long rectangular tables placed end to end. Each team's head coach sat in the order he would be drafting, beginning with the team that had finished with the worst record the year before. Frank counted off fifteen picks ahead of him. Some coaches would take their sons in the first round, especially if they had been an All-Star in the younger league.

After brief introductions and a summation of the draft rules, the first pick was made. Because most coaches knew who they were going to choose first, the picks happened in rapid-fire.

"Anyone know this Mac kid?" one coach, two picks ahead of Frank, asked. "He looked pretty good out there, but I just don't know him." It was a foolish question. No one was going to share player information this early in the draft. Most assuredly, some of the coaches had targeted Big Mac as a sleeper pick in the second or third round. The inquisitive coach passed on Mac, and Frank felt his heart beating out of his chest.

When it was his pick, Frank wasted no time saying, "I'll take Mac."

Hands pounded the table. "I knew I should have picked him," one coach lamented.

"What do you know about him, Frank?" another coach asked from across the table.

"He's coming over from Midland," Frank said. "I met his dad at Baseball Dreams." A round of groans followed but did not linger.

"The rich just get richer," one coach lamented. It was only the first round, and there was a lot of baseball talent still available. After choosing Big Mac, Frank picked up an All-Star center fielder who went by the nickname Tank. Doc had liked a boy named Patrick, who went by P-Mac, and Frank envisioned the sure-handed blond in a platoon situation at third base. Frank got both of them in the draft.

Stepping into the cool night air after the draft, Frank called Doc and said, "I got Big Mac."

Quoting a famous line from the television show *The A-Team*, Doc said, "I love it when a plan comes together."

🏐🏐🏐

The Sharks finished that season 20-0 and won the division. Big Mac, Killer, KJ, Jet, and Snooky all made the All-Star team, which Frank and Doc coached. All five had more than twenty hits on the season – an average of more than one per game.

The team outscored its opponents 208-53, allowing an average of fewer than three runs per game. Big Mac and Killer, as the primary pitchers, combined to throw four shutouts, and only one opponent scored more than five runs in a game. All pitchers, which included both KJ and Snooky, had a 2.06 ERA for the season. Overall, the team hit for a .338 average. On defense, they averaged less than two errors per game, including six error-free games, and posted a .931 fielding percentage.

Big Mac led the team in hitting, on-base percentage, slugging percentage, and contact percentage. His batting average was .543 on the year, and KJ finished second at .511. Big Mac, Killer, Jet, and Snooky all finished with fewer than ten strikeouts in twenty games. Jet, in the leadoff spot, scored thirty-six runs that season and scored 94 percent of the times he reached first base. Killer, batting second, scored thirty-one runs, and the two benefitted from Snooky's thirty-eight RBIs in the number three hole.

Killer was the starter in most games, and Big Mac was the closer. The big lefty struck out sixty-eight in only thirty-five innings pitched, and opponents had a .141 batting average against him.

Frank had nicknames for all of them: Jet, Tank, A-Rod, Killer, Big Mac, P-Mac, Stretch, Pops, BP, Sarge, Snooky, and KJ.

While another team finished undefeated the following year, the Sharks 20-0 record was the first undefeated season anyone in the league could remember for that age level.

In his funeral home office, Doc had three framed photographs on a bookshelf. There was a 5 x 7 photograph of the undefeated team. Next to that 5 x 7 were two larger, framed 8 x 10 photographs – each a photograph of the two teams preceding the undefeated team. On their shoulders, the great team was built.

The Braves were down 3-2 going into the bottom of the ninth inning. The fans who had been lulled to baseball boredom over the game's first seven innings were now wide awake and rocking. The war chant and tomahawk chop, both coming during the Braves 1991 worst-to-first season, reached a feverish pitch.

"This is why you stay until the end," Frank said to Phil. "This is what makes baseball so wonderful. Anything can happen." He knew it was true on every level of the sport.

Pinch hitter Matt Diaz singled to open the frame for the Braves and was replaced by pinch runner Pete Orr. The Braves leadoff hitter, Marcus Giles, who had committed three errors in the game, sacrificed Orr to second. Orr then stole third, putting the tying run only ninety feet away. Chipper Jones, in the number three hole, then grounded out, scoring Orr to tie the game.

"Free baseball!" the boys' dad said out loud in front of Frank as the inning ended.

Sitting to Frank's left, Bradley said to Whitney, "Are you ready to go?"

She looked at him in disbelief, and Frank laughed to himself. "Hell no," she said, and then smiled sheepishly at the little boys in front of her. "I'm sorry for saying that."

The dad turned his head in her direction and said, "They've heard a lot worse."

The stadium was rocking as the remaining crowd settled in for extra innings.

EXTRA INNINGS
GOOD-BYE

The tenth inning was scoreless, and Frank was wondering how late this game would go. He looked at his watch. If it went past eleven, he would get a hotel room on the east side of Atlanta, call Vicki, and just make the rest of the drive in the morning.

In the top of the eleventh, Marlin's first baseman Mike Jacobs walked and scored the go-ahead run, putting the Marlins up 4-3. Jacobs had enjoyed a big night. His two-run single in the eighth had given the Marlins their first lead of the game.

Fans started streaming out of Turner Field. The Braves might have come back once in the bottom of the ninth, but expecting a second comeback was perhaps a bridge too far. Frank knew it too. There had been many games when he left after seven innings, tuning in to the radio broadcast as he started the drive back to South Carolina.

But tonight, he stayed. He wanted to see every single out regardless of the expense or the cost to his body. He thought, even if he broke down and spent the night on the side of lonely Interstate 20, it would all be worth it to see every last pitch. He settled in with his scorebook and the Black Warrior pencil.

The Marlins took their 4-3 lead into the Braves bottom of the eleventh. Those remaining were nervous and quiet. Frank saw fans packing up souvenirs all around him just in case this was the end of it.

Frank closed his eyes. He wanted to remember every sound around him – the organ, the chants, the loudspeaker, the tomahawk chop – and remember every smell. He had done this before – when he had said good-bye to baseball.

⚾ ⚾ ⚾

Following the Sharks' undefeated season, the All-Star season was over almost before it started. In the first tournament, the All-Stars cruised to a championship. Then, with high hopes in the second-tier tournament, the All-Stars were defeated in two quick games and then dispersed to their summer. Expectations had been so high, but Frank was not surprised. The Concord season was so long and so intense that many All-Star teams often flamed out before they got started.

"In Concord," he told Doc, "it's about the pride of making the All-Star team and not necessarily playing in All-Star tournaments." It was not to say that Concord was without its championship All-Star teams; a handful had played in a Dixie World Series as the South Carolina champion, and a few of those had won the national championship. Frank's youngest son had played on a state championship All-Star team, and another had played in two state tournaments.

After that undefeated season, Frank coached another handful of years, helping out with a team here or there. On paper, he was the head coach of a Pony League team for two years, but in reality, he did little more than set the lineup, keep the scorebook, and manage the paperwork for the team. He recruited younger men to run practices. His very last team competed for the division championship before running out of steam at the end of the season. Doc came to the occasional practice, but just as a spectator. The undefeated season was his last one as Frank's assistant. Pecker had also left after the undefeated season, but remained a colorful fixture at the ballpark. More than once he had jumped into Frank's dugout when an assistant couldn't be at a game. Little Wood was now playing football, and Pecker was compelled to support his son as much as possible.

When Frank's Sharks lost 8-5 to Biscuit Shack in the playoffs during Frank's final season, ending his long career, both Doc and Pecker were in the stands. They sat near the dugout, and Frank talked to them occasionally during the game. After the loss, both men met him coming out of the dugout. Vicki joined them there, too, and Frank hugged her.

"Good job," she said.

Frank sighed. "End of an era," he said. She hugged him again.

"The scoreboard turns off for everyone, Coach Frank," Doc said, extending a hand that became a hug. "It's been a lot of years since that day we met out at Round Top Baptist Church and the Field of Dreams."

Frank smiled. "Yep, it has."

There was awkward silence – that awkward silence that comes with friends, bound by activity or Sunday school, wanting to say they will stay in touch, but knowing they probably won't ever be that close again.

"Coach Frank," Pecker said, puffing up his chest, "thank you is about all I can say. To both of you, I just want to say thank you. You've both been real friends to me, and being around all those boys gave me some purpose. It also let me spend real quality time with Little Wood."

Frank hugged him, and it was clear that Pecker was not one who experienced a lot of hugs. He pushed out of the hug pretty quickly.

"Keep it G-rated, Coach Frank," he said, laughing. "No butt grabbing."

Doc gave the little man a side hug and said, "Lord, Lord, what a character you are, Willet J. Wood. I'm going to miss you, brother."

"Well, Doc, I would say that I hope to see you around, but I don't," Pecker said. "The last thing I want to think about is you standing over my dead body, getting ready to fill 'er up with high test for a hole in the ground."

Doc shoved him and laughed.

"I want to tell you both how much I appreciate you," Frank said. "Doc, we never would have had all the success without you. I appreciate you sticking with me. Willet, that day you jumped out of that F-250 was an important day. Our practices and games were a lot more fun with you as part of them. Can you imagine if it had just been me and this mortician here?"

"I hear that," Pecker said. "Thank you, Frank. Thank you again."

The three men and Vicki started toward the parking lot, and Frank saw a game wrapping up on an adjacent field. He dropped the equipment bag in the grass and said, "Vicki, let's go over and watch this game finish out. Do you guys mind if we do that?"

"No, sir," Pecker said. "I need to get home anyway."

"Give me one more hug," Doc said, pulling his friend close. "The Lord used us in a lot of ways, Frank." He pulled back and hugged Vicki. "Let's meet at Applebee's one day soon." He turned and walked toward the parking lot.

Frank and Vicki walked closer to the minor league field, where the game was wrapping up the final inning. Players were chanting little cheers from both dugouts. A late-inning comeback was underway in a key playoff game; Frank looked over the complex, which was bursting with energy on a Saturday night. It reminded him of a night at the Acorn County Fair when he was a boy.

"I'm going to watch how this game ends," he said.

"I have nowhere else to be," Vicki said. "In fact, I feel more at home here than I do at our home sometimes based on the time we've spent between the two places."

A little boy, probably a T-ball player, ran beside them, holding a half-eaten corn dog. He was catching up to a friend, who was wearing another team's uniform. The boys put their arms around one another's shoulders and walked together in the direction of the ballpark's playground.

"That's sweet," Vicki said.

Standing by the fence, Frank watched a team complete its comeback victory. A parent sitting near Frank said to him, "That's a great way to end the season. One of the team's weakest hitters gets a base hit to score the winning run."

Frank watched as that winning team gathered with its coach for a postgame meeting in shallow left field. The coach gave the game ball to the player who had the winning hit. All of his friends slapped him on the back and cheered.

"Baseball is full of surprises," Frank said. "That's what makes it so special." He turned to leave the ballpark for the last time as a coach. He stood there and closed his eyes, taking in the smells and the noise. He heard two little boys negotiating a sleepover with parents. He heard a little boy praising the postgame snack and then offering some of it to his little brother. There was the familiar click-clack of the older boys' metal cleats on the sidewalk. The pull chain of the United States flag gently tapped the flagpole. He opened his eyes to see players from both of the playoff teams – winners and losers – now racing the bases of the field where they had just competed. From somewhere a football appeared, and dozens of boys now gathered for a quick football game as parents shouted for them to "come on, let's go."

"Are you sad?" Vicki whispered as Frank now grabbed the equipment bag and walked out into the parking lot.

"All those years, I knew this day would come," he said. "I'm not sure what I'll do next."

He stopped to see two men leaning on an outfield fence. One of them was a league board member, and the other was a coach, and they reminded him of the conversation he had with Terry Thompson long ago in Jenson, after the scrimmage against Burger King.

"I'll bet you coach the rest of your life," Terry Thompson once told him. "Just remember, in my experience, the best coaches know it's never about the baseball – not really. It's about the boys."

Frank had stared into Terry's face as he spoke those words. "If I do coach for a long time, how will I know when it's time to stop?"

"You will know," Terry said. "You will know when it's time to step aside and let a younger Frank Wilcox have his turn."

⚾ ⚾ ⚾

Chipper Jones had not homered in his previous seventy at-bats.

He came to bat in the eleventh inning and hammered Randy Messenger's first-pitch fastball over the right-center field wall for a three-run walk-off home run. The win was the Braves' seventh win in nine games, and four of those wins had come in dramatic comeback fashion.

The remaining fans were on their feet. Phil slapped Frank on the back. The little boys in front of him gave one another high fives. The dad turned to Frank and gave him a high five slap to the right hand. Bradley already had Whitney walking up the aisle before any of the celebratory guys could give her a hug that might last a little too long. Frank looked toward the aisle, and she looked back and gave a thumbs-up, acknowledging the celebration. She pointed to his jacket neatly folded on the back of the chair. Frank turned and shook the couple's hands behind him.

The woman's gaze locked with Frank's, and she said, "We enjoyed visiting with you during the game. Will you forgive an old woman and let me ask you something?"

Frank smiled at her.

"How can I pray for you?"

Frank sighed and looked upward, toward the dark sky above Turner Field. He looked back at the kind face. Her husband was looking at him, smiling too. He was slowly nodding his head, acknowledging that this was how his sweet wife lived her life – gently, authentically, prayerfully.

"I came to this game looking for a little peace," Frank said. "I miss my boys terribly. I miss the noise around our house. I miss the ballpark, where I coached, and I miss the families I once loved out there. I'm just kind of lost, and I need to pull out of this funk. Being at this game has helped."

She smiled at him. "I will pray for you to have peace. You know, you've got another chapter of your life to start. Right here in these stands, the Lord is saying, 'It's time to get that chapter started.'"

Frank felt an uncomfortable wave of emotion and twisted his mouth to the right to fight back a tear. "Thank you," he said. "Thank you so much for telling me that." She patted him on the shoulder, and the couple started for the end of the row and the exit stairs. He shook the older man's hand.

As Chipper crossed home plate, Frank gathered his scorebook and Dippin' Dots helmet and started out of Turner Field. It was going to be a long ride home, but in some inexplicable way, he felt purged and at peace. At the Madison, Georgia, rest stop, he pulled off Interstate 20, sat in his car, and smiled. It had been a great day. Back on the interstate, he cranked up ZZ Top, cracked the windows halfway, and put the truck on cruise control.

POSTGAME

The Braves game had been just the therapy Frank needed.

It had allowed him to meet new people, be encouraged by them, see a great baseball game, and reminisce about the great days around baseball, the boys, and the ballpark environment.

Vicki noticed a much better attitude. He laughed more, and he made her laugh. She told a friend, "Thank goodness, Frank has his laugh back. He was getting on my nerves."

As he went about his piddling in the backyard, she noticed him out at the graveyard, where all the old baseball equipment had been abandoned under the big cedar tree. She watched as he stood there, staring into the corner, perhaps wondering what to do or where to begin.

Frank pulled out the old pitchback used for defensive work. The stretched fabric was rotten in places, but Frank still went inside for his catcher's mitt and tossed some balls at the contraption. He immediately regretted doing so, feeling the fire from in his wrists. He pushed through the pain, realizing that if he threw to just the right spot, there was still enough tension in the netting to throw the ball back at his waist.

Vicki eased outside without him noticing her.

"Having fun?" she asked.

"When we were little boys, our daddy bought one of these for Jack and me," Frank said. "It wasn't this sturdy, but it did the same thing. It's like an artificial friend with whom to play catch. Jack and I used it as a hitter. We put it behind home plate and then pitched to it. The ball would fly out into the yard; we'd run it down and play this imaginary baseball game. This one sure served our boys well."

He threw another ball at the thing, and it sailed through the rotten fabric to an oak tree in the backyard.

"I can probably get online and find a replacement netting for it," he said. "It's worth keeping around for the grandkids one day."

"Have fun, Frank," she said. "It will be great if you can clean out all that stuff back there." She walked back into the house.

The old SoloHitter was a more difficult project to remove. Old, thick kudzu vines had found the large-piped equipment with a ball dangling from elastic. Hitters could hit the ball and then wait on it to snap back into place for another hit. Frank used hedge clippers to free the SoloHitter from its shackles but then realized he had to cut the vines further back to remove it from their wicked clutches. It was a lot of work. Out in the yard, he realized that the metal piping had rusty holes in it. He pulled it aside for removal to the county recycling center.

He removed the old baseball bats and lined them up side by side in the center of the yard. He took a picture of them and sent it to his boys by text message. Almost immediately, they began responding, matching seasons and key at-bats with each piece of metal. He picked out three or four he knew were used to hit home runs and stuck those inside his wooden shed. He also kept his oldest son's first bat, a Louisville Slugger, that had cost him $150. He thought that price was absurd at the time, but as the years progressed, the amount he spent on bats and gloves steadily climbed.

"That was obscene," he said to himself, remembering the expensive equipment. He remembered justifying it with an analogy of learning to drive on the I-285 perimeter highway around Atlanta.

"At the time, the speed limit on that highway was 55," he had told some friends when discussing the justification for expensive equipment. "Everyone drove 70. Everyone knew that driving 70 was dangerous. Everyone knew that driving was 70 was against the law. Everyone knew that if they didn't drive 70, they would get run over. If you don't keep up, you fall behind. If you fall behind, there's no catching up. Everyone must decide the risk and reward for themselves, and if it doesn't add up, you get off the highway."

Within a week of getting the new $150 bat, his son left it at a Sunday picnic at a Georgia state park – ninety miles west from Concord. The boy did not realize he had left the bat until they got all the way home that evening, and by that time, it was too late to return to the state park. So the next morning, Frank was on the road, driving back across the Savannah River to the park, where he found the bat exactly where his boys had been playing baseball.

Vicki returned to the backyard, this time to sit in the sun and watch him work.

"How's it going out here?" she asked. Frank was hot and sweaty and tired from working to reclaim the graveyard.

"I'm keeping the old pitchback – just long enough to see if I can refurbish it," he said. "If not, I'll get rid of it."

"It should make you feel better to have all of this junk out of here," she said.

He walked into the wooden shed and came back with two large equipment bags. He opened them and removed old shin guards, catcher's chest protectors and helmets, small metal pitch counters, and even a stopwatch that he often used for the predraft player assessments.

"I don't know what to do with all this stuff," he said. He pulled out an old catcher's mitt that he wasn't completely sure was his. It was dry-rotting from years of neglect. "All those years, I just accumulated stuff. It's like a giant lost and found."

"Is that your mitt?" she asked.

"No!" he said, mildly offended. "My Nokona is in the office, oiled and ready to go."

She rolled her eyes at his indignation.

"There's a bunch of old gloves in the attic," she said. "I'm pretty sure they don't belong to the boys – just gloves that came to our house over all those seasons."

Frank went to the attic and pulled down two small moving boxes full of old, musty, stiff baseball gloves. Most had been used by his boys, but there were several with no identification. Frank was pretty sure they had been left at the Field of Dreams and then never claimed.

"At least they are leather," he said, holding up one to Vicki. "Damn Walmart gloves. Parents would send their boys to play baseball with plastic-coated gloves from Walmart – or Target. There's no way a boy can succeed in playing baseball with plastic. I ought to clean these up and give them away."

"You should," she said. "Some of the men from the church are going on a mission trip next month to Africa, and they might like the gloves to give out to children. You might even take them to the league's registration next spring and make them available to little boys who don't have a glove. There might be a player who needs a good glove." She paused, wickedly smiled, and then said, "They certainly can't use one of those inferior gloves from Walmart." She bowed her head in reverence and laughed, and that made Frank laugh out loud too.

Further cleaning, Frank dug out the old rubber hitting tees and a broken contraption that served as a manual pitching machine. He thought the pitching machine might be worth restoring and donating to someone. The rubber hitting tees were shot, and he threw them in the back of the truck.

The last thing to go was the old Instructoswing. It always made him smile. Noodle's dad always helped out at practice, and Doc always assigned him to work with players using the Instructoswing. The dad good-naturedly complained about the task but was always faithful to help out. Now, Frank cut away vines to free the Instructoswing. The protective rubber around the two bars through which players hit was decayed, and without it, the expensive aluminum bats would be destroyed. When he freed it, Frank tossed it into the back of his truck for disposal.

He looked at Vicki and laughed. "I wonder if Steve would like the Instructoswing as an heirloom?" He laughed at the idea.

At the end of the weekend, the graveyard was cleaned out, and while there was work still to be done back there, Frank could envision the shady corner as a fun place for grandchildren to play one day. It was all cathartic. He felt good. Singing the famous Bob Seger song, Frank admitted that he had indeed "turned the page."

He looked over all the old equipment once used to help hundreds of boys become better baseball players. Frank smiled and said out loud, "Lord, I hope I made a difference." Deep within, he felt an answer.

You did. You all did. Be at peace.

⚾ ⚾ ⚾

Not long after Frank cleaned out the backyard graveyard, he sat down to open his social media account and read what friends and acquaintances were posting. In the top right corner there was the unmistakable red numeral indicating that he had a friend request. He clicked on the icon and smiled to himself.

"I'll be darned," he said.

It was Joel – the catcher from his very first team in Jenson – now decades ago. Frank looked at the man's face and then looked over at the boy's face from the team photograph on his desk. He could see a resemblance, even if he might not recognize Joel on the street somewhere.

He accepted the friend request.

Frank sent him a message, reintroducing himself.

It was not necessary. Joel remembered the trip to Waycross for the new catcher's equipment. Frank reminded him how important he was to the team.

Joel wrote back, "I actually worked for Rayonier for ten years, and now they are a customer of mine. I recall the trip to the sporting goods store in Waycross to purchase new catcher's equipment. I would like to say that I got extremely good at baseball, but that would be a stretch. But life has been good. I've raised two daughters and have no complaints."

In a future message, he included a photograph of his green-and-yellow Rayonier jersey – his mom had kept it. Frank returned a photograph of the coffee mug that Joel had given him as a gift at the team's year-end party.

The communication with his first catcher caused Frank to rinse out the coffee mug and put it on his desk.

⚾ ⚾ ⚾

A few days after hearing from Joel, Frank visited an Episcopal church in downtown Columbia – just twelve miles east of Concord. A bulletin board caught his attention, and on that bulletin board, he recognized a name. It was Sarge – the second baseman whose bunt had scored the winning run in the Miracle in May.

He went by the church's office, and a kind secretary called the boy's home. He was there. She told him his former coach, Frank Wilcox, was at the church and asked about him.

Frank concluded his visit by meeting with the rector and was about to leave when he noticed a friendly face walking down a hallway to see him.

"Sarge," he said, smiling.

"Hi, Coach," the man said. The two of them reminisced about the two years Sarge played for the Sharks, including his bunt single that won the miracle game.

"I knew I had to get that bunt down and get to first as fast as I could," Sarge said.

"Doc always said teaching you to bunt was once of the smartest things we did," Frank said. "You played a great second base that year too."

"That year I played second, I could hear you yelling, 'Down and ready,' in my sleep," Sarge said, laughing. "One game, I kicked a ball that I should have fielded. I heard you yell at me all the way across the field."

Frank winced. "I'm sorry about that," he said.

"No, don't apologize," Sarge said. "I loved those two years. I believe we won thirty-five games over those two seasons, and one championship. No apologies needed for that success."

⚾⚾⚾

Frank stood inside the restaurant in downtown Columbia. It was lunchtime, but the lunch crowd had not yet trickled inside. The door swung open, and in walked a friendly face – effervescent, beaming.

"Hey, Coach," the man shook Frank's hand, and the two men hugged one another.

"SpongeBob," Frank said, and then sort of half-apologized. "You probably don't want to be called that anymore, but you'll always be SpongeBob to me."

"Are you kidding?" the young man said. "I love it! A nickname from Coach Frank was like gold."

The two sat, ate lunch, and talked for about ninety minutes. They reminisced about SpongeBob jumping third base, Big D encouraging him in the playoff game, and Frank taking the gum away.

"My dad's favorite story is when you took the gum away," SpongeBob said. "I was just so excited to pitch, and someone gave me gum to calm my nerves." He laughed. "I don't think I did that badly, pitching."

"No, you didn't," Frank said.

"I was not a good hitter when I played for you," the young man said. "I became a better hitter the older I got, and I was able to play for several more years at the ballpark. I even pitched a lot more, and I got better at it. I look at those two years playing for you as giving me a foundation to do what I loved as a kid. I still love baseball."

They talked about family and jobs, and the visit was over all too soon.

"I'd like to have a reunion out at the Field of Dreams," Frank said.

"Let me know," SpongeBob said. "I'll be there!"

⚾ ⚾ ⚾

One afternoon, Frank was in the Food Lion grocery store. He was drifting through the aisle of canned vegetables and tomato sauce, aimlessly staring at the cans and hoping to be inspired with a plan for supper. As he approached the end of the aisle, he was startled by a hulk of a figure.

"Hey, Coach." The friendly voice was quiet – just above a whisper.

It was Big D, dressed in the uniform of the Army National Guard.

Frank reached out his hand, and the big man's handshake swallowed it.

"How are you doing?" Big D asked, and Frank was overcome by how genuine and kind the words were. Time had not changed the demeanor of the boy he once knew.

"I'm well," Frank said. "Empty nest and cleaning out all the old baseball gear."

"You aren't coaching anymore?" Big D asked, smiling.

Frank shook his head no. "Time for younger men to do it."

"You were the best," Big D said. "I only played that one year for you, but you and Doc were the best."

Frank learned that the big man was married, and Frank shared SpongeBob's memory of Big D's encouragement after the left field error. Big D smiled and looked away, asking how and what SpongeBob was doing.

"I remember the maxims," Big D said. "You reminded us to encourage others at every practice and game. I remember thinking that your advice was the same advice my dad gave me, so I tried my best to lift others."

Frank smiled.

"I am so, so proud of you."

The big man smiled in an embarrassed kind of way, and the two parted company.

It made Frank's entire day to see him.

⚾ ⚾ ⚾

Frank was in a Mobile, Alabama hotel room. It was raining outside. He was in Mobile on business, and he missed Vicki. He had settled into an evening of quiet reading when his telephone startled him with both a loud ringtone and a vibration across the wooden coffee table.

He picked up the telephone and stared at the number. He didn't recognize it, and the caller was not in his list of mobile contacts. Uncharacteristically, he answered it.

"Is this Frank Wilcox?" a man's voice spoke.

"It is," Frank said.

"Coach, you may not remember me, but my name is John, and I played shortstop for you many years ago in Stanton, Georgia."

Frank's mouth dropped. It had been thirty-five years since he lived in Stanton, and he had not spoken to any of his former players since leaving there. John had played shortstop one year, the year of the Weapon, and it was John who led the team in hitting.

"I do remember you," Frank said. "I went on to coach about twenty-five years, and only two players ever came close to your batting average. You hit .545 that season. I never saw anything like it."

There was a pause.

"You know what I remember?" the voice said. "I remember striking out and coming back to the bench. I was upset because there was a man on third and I watched the third strike. I knew you didn't like that. You stopped me and said, 'Everyone strikes out. Don't worry about striking out. Get out there and play defense. You will get a hit next time.' That's what I remember. You told me not to worry about making mistakes."

Frank smiled in the dark hotel room. He didn't remember that but was glad it had made an impact.

Frank said, "It's a reminder that people remember the little things we say and do."

John agreed. He and his family lived out West but were moving to the Northeastern United States soon. He was an educator, and Frank was not surprised to learn that.

Frank asked him about other players on that team – players John would have grown up with after Frank left Stanton. John remembered many of his old teammates but had lost contact with them. He knew Jeffrey, the catcher, was still in Stanton, and Frank was able to find him on Facebook. Jeffrey now worked for the university there. John didn't know the whereabouts of Charles or Sam. Frank did find Del, who had played shortstop for Frank's second team in Stanton and was the team's MVP that year.

"We had the best coach in all of Stanton," John said. "It was more than just something to do, and everyone knew that about you. Because it was important to you, it became important to all of us."

When Frank got off the telephone, he sat in the dark of the hotel room. He had given up reading. He was alive with all the fun memories of coaching those two seasons in Stanton.

⚾ ⚾ ⚾

Frank likened social media to a giant Rolodex and used social media to find many of his former players. Sugarman and his wife had started a nonprofit arts company in Cincinnati, and Sugarman was pursuing an MBA. Hoss was an attorney in Memphis, specializing in estate law. Mark, another catcher, worked at Watertight, the family business and the Shark's sponsor during two championship seasons. Big A and Big G were both physicians. Snooky was a civil engineer in North Carolina. E-Mar, whose twin killing won the All-Star tournament game against Ameriland, was now a physical therapist and owned his practice. Several players had joined the military; most of them were starting families.

Frank and Vicki attended Hammer's wedding. The newlyweds moved within walking distance of Frank's house, and within a few years, Frank opened the front door to see his former first baseman standing outside with a baby in a stroller.

"Hey, Coach," Hammer said. "I was out on a walk with Ezra and thought we would drop by and see if you were home."

Frank sat on the front steps of his home and visited in the beautiful fall sunshine.

Hammer and Sugarman, Frank learned, had played eight seasons together at the ballpark, and that was quite a feat, considering the complexities of the draft every two years as players advanced to a new age level. In addition to two championships in the youngest league and the championship with Coach Frank, the two had been a part of a league championship in their last year of junior high school. Hammer played first base all of those years, and Sugarman locked down second base.

"I still talk to Sugarman on occasion," Hammer said. "He will always be my oldest friend. We had some crazy times, even beyond the baseball field."

The visit continued with Frank promising to come out of retirement one day when Ezra started playing baseball. "I can at least sit in the dugout and tell your players to stop being goofy." Frank laughed.

"I wouldn't think of coaching without you, Coach Frank," Hammer said.

Frank was working, typing a letter, when his mobile telephone rang. It was a local number, and against his better judgment, he answered the telephone.

"This is Frank Wilcox," he said into the device.

"Coach Frank, this is Ace," the young man said.

"Well, Ace," Frank said. "How in the world are you doing?"

"I'm fine, Coach," he said. Nervous chit-chat followed before the boy got to the reason for his call. "I heard that you officiate weddings, and I wonder if you will officiate one for me and my girlfriend."

"Who in the world is marrying you?" Frank asked, laughing.

There was laughter on the other end.

"Her name is Jan, and we are looking at next fall," he said. "It would be an honor if you would officiate it. Neither of us really has a church or pastor, and honestly, you were always kind of that person for me anyway."

"Listen, I'm the one who is honored," Frank said. "But you have to agree to meet with me and Vicki a few times beforehand. I want to make sure you and Jan know what marriage is all about."

"That sounds great, Coach," he said. "Maybe I can bring my glove and we can throw some too."

"I would love that," Frank said. "Let's set things up."

JP had become a musician. Aside from his full-time job, he and his wife served their church's music ministry and regularly performed at venues around central North Carolina. While he was playing one

Friday evening, Frank and Vicki slipped in to enjoy his show – a show that included some covers and original songs he had written.

JP recognized him as soon as he walked in the door, and between songs introduced him to the gathering crowd. At a set break, JP and his wife joined Vicki and Frank at a table.

"Coach Frank!" JP said. "This is a great surprise."

"I've meant to take off one weekend to hear you play, and this seemed like a good time," Frank said.

They talked briefly.

"Those two years were my favorites of all the ones at the ball-park," JP said, and then laughed. "To this day, I can't hear KC & the Sunshine Band without thinking of batting practice."

"That year you pitched – that was my best year coaching," Frank said. "We didn't have a team full of All-Stars, but we had pitching, and that kept us competitive. Doc and I had to work hard. That year, you struck out an average of twelve per game – best percentage of any pitcher I ever coached. You were so efficient."

"That Sunday finish in May was unbelievable," he said.

"The Miracle in May," Frank said.

JP looked over his shoulder at the stage. "I gotta get back to it."

"Absolutely," Frank said.

JP took the stage and easily played the first several lines of "(Shake, Shake, Shake) Shake Your Booty" while saying, "Everyone. A big shout out to one of the best baseball coaches in South Carolina – Frank Wilcox. He coached me when I was ten years old. We won about thirty games in two years, and we took batting practice to this little tune." He pointed to Frank, who smiled. The crowd modestly clapped.

⚾ ⚾ ⚾

Frank wondered what had become of Jet – the fastest boy he had ever coached. It didn't take long to find him on social media, and Frank sent him a message. The reply came back quickly.

He, too, remembered KC & the Sunshine Band even though he played seven years after JP, Hammer, and Sugarman played. Rock and roll had become a Coach Frank staple for working a team out of a hitting slump.

"After the ballpark was renovated before that undefeated season, we had the very first game on a brand-new field," Jet said. "In the top of the first inning, I was playing second. There was a runner on first, and I got him on a force out at second. You made a big deal about me getting the very first putout on the new field. I would never have thought much about it, but you made that one play pretty special, and I've never forgotten it.

"There was also the practice that I was a little late arriving," he said. "I was eating beef jerky in mom's SUV and got choked. You fussed because I was late, saying, 'We can't practice without our second baseman.' When I told you that I was choking on beef jerky, everyone laughed and called me Jerky the rest of the practice rather than Jet."

Frank didn't remember it but laughed all the same.

"Coach, every time I got on base, the dugout would cheer, 'We got some speed on base, we got some speed on base. We got some S-P-double E-D speed on base.' I was determined to score. That did so much for my confidence."

⚾ ⚾ ⚾

Frank was mowing the grass one afternoon when his music playlist was interrupted by a telephone call. It was Big Mac, who Frank had plucked from the draft to complete the undefeated team.

"I was just thinking of you, Coach Frank," he said. Frank knew the big lefty had played baseball in high school and college, and had heard he was playing independent baseball beyond South Carolina.

"I'm trying to improve and work my way closer to home," he said.

"I'm proud of you," Frank said. "I'm proud of the man you are."

"Coach Frank," Mac said, "I often think about that season. That season had a big place in my life and baseball development. I was nervous coming over from Midland, and I didn't know any of the other boys on the team. It was awesome because everyone just accepted me right away; you and the others made me feel like I belonged from day one. I'll never forget those practices at the Field of Dreams. It was a great year and put my baseball success in motion. You were a great coach."

⚾ ⚾ ⚾

One Saturday afternoon, Frank walked into a local hardware store looking for a new socket set. Absent-mindedly, over many years, he had lost a bit here and there and now needed a brand-new set. Frank was looking at options when he noticed a young man at the end of the long row of tools. The man was looking over a selection of drills and drill bits.

Frank chose his socket set. It was a good one, a decent one, but not one of the costly high-end sets. He didn't depend on sockets for his livelihood – just for projects around the house. He walked down the row, excused himself as he passed between the man and the power drills, and then walked on toward the checkout.

Frank paid for the sockets and then walked out of the small hardware store near his home. He was a few feet from his truck when he heard a voice behind him, "Coach Frank?"

He turned to see the man who had been studying the drills. Frank now had a full look at him. He was just a bit shorter than Frank, lean and muscular. He had a beard and wore a dirty Patagonia-branded cap. Frank stared at him hard, trying to place him.

The man smiled, realizing Frank didn't recognize the boy within him.

"It's me, Richie," he said, shaking his head. "My nickname was Foxy. I'm the one who stopped practice for the dead fox." Frank walked to him and stuck out his hand for a shake.

"My goodness, the beard and hat threw me," Frank said. "I can see you in there now." They laughed. "What are you doing these days?"

"I work for my family's construction business," he said. "You may remember that my dad helped my grandfather build houses, and now I help too."

Frank nodded. It was coming back to him.

"Coach," Foxy stammered as if he was clearing his throat, "I've never forgotten how you prayed for my grandfather that day at the team party. I didn't have a lot of people around me who prayed a lot, and I've never forgotten you for, I don't know, the boldness. Things haven't been great for me in recent years, but they seem to be turning a corner." He looked toward the horizon before turning back. "It was a tough divorce."

"Foxy," Frank smiled as he said it, "we all have valleys. I've been going through my own lately – especially since my boys moved away and I stopped coaching. I guess I'm just way too sentimental. It's been somewhat tough getting started in the new chapter of my life. Seeing you today has helped a lot."

"Coach Frank—" he paused "—can I pray for you?"

Right there, in the hardware store parking lot, a former player prayed for his former coach. It wasn't a long prayer, but it was just right, and Frank felt tears filling his eyes as the young man prayed for his coach's peace of mind and for him to experience joy in the Lord. Frank had barely lifted his head when he felt the man's hug embrace him.

"Thank you, Foxy," Frank said, hugging him back.

"I want to show you something, Coach," Foxy said, and started toward his truck. He opened the driver's-side door, reached across to the glove compartment, popped it open, and returned holding an old, dirty baseball. He handed it to Frank, who turned it over in his hands.

As Frank looked at the ball, Foxy said, "My second year on your Sharks. We were playing Hardee's. It was the bottom of the sixth, and we were winning by one run. They had the tying run on third and the winning run on second. We had two outs on them – one more and we win the game."

Frank enjoyed hearing him tell the story.

"I was in left field, and you were outside our dugout coaching the defense," he said. "They had a good hitter coming up, and you walked down the line toward me in the outfield. You said, 'Foxy, he may pull it to you. He's hit it out here twice before. Just relax and catch it.'"

"You just turned around and walked back to the dugout," Foxy said. "You seemed so sure I was going to catch it."

Frank said, "I remember. He hit the ball to you in left field, and you caught the fly ball for the third out. We won the game. You were the hero."

"And you gave me that game ball at the next practice," Foxy said. "Read it."

Frank looked at his handwriting on the ball:

Game Ball. 5-12-2002. Sharks 6, Hardees 5.

Foxy. 1-2, 2 runs scored and caught final out in left field.

Frank looked up. He smiled.

"Read that last line," the man said.

Frank read it out loud, "Foxy, we won because of you."

Frank handed it back to him.

"Coach Frank, I keep this ball in my truck as a reminder," he said. "It reminds me that I may be out there all alone just like in left field, and life may hit something my way, but I can handle it. I can make the play. I can win, and I can help others win too."

"You sure took a big lesson from that game ball," Frank said, smiling. "I'll bet most of them are long gone."

"Coach, you were never goofy and silly," Foxy said. "You talked to us like we were adults, but you remembered we were just boys. You were especially kind to boys like me who weren't good enough to be All-Stars."

Frank said, "To be honest, my favorite baseball was in the fall when we didn't even turn on the scoreboard. There was no pressure."

Frank was getting teary-eyed behind his sunglasses.

"Thank you, Foxy," Frank said. "It's blessed my entire week seeing you here today." He got the young man's mobile telephone number and texted him, so the man had his number too. "Let me know how I can pray for you or encourage you going forward."

"Same," Foxy said. They embraced again and then shook hands again. "I've gotta get back to work." He got in his truck, and Frank walked to his own truck.

"Thank you, Lord," Frank said out loud. "Thank you."

⚾ ⚾ ⚾

Frank Wilcox left retirement.

He refurbished the old pitchback used for teaching defensive drills. In the back corner of his shed, he found a PVC hitting tee that was in surprisingly good shape, shielded from the sun for several years. He cleaned it up as best he could. In the attic, he discovered an old stash of tennis balls that he had used to teach boys how to catch fly balls. All of this equipment gave him an idea.

He might not be able to coach teams any longer, but perhaps there were children in need of a coach – even a coach whose eyes were still hidden by sunglasses he always wore on baseball fields. They were prescription glasses – he actually needed them to see.

Frank reached out to the local recreation department and let it be known that he was available to help anyone under the age of ten at no charge. He would gladly help any child so long as their parents stayed with them at the practice sessions, because Frank felt parents needed to learn too.

The first call came from a single mom, Sheila, whose little boy Ellis was six and playing T-ball. She didn't know anything about sports, and her little boy seemed lost on the field with other boys and their dads running around. "Sometimes he just stands there all alone."

He had cried and wanted to quit.

"Don't let him quit," Frank said over the telephone. "He needs to be a part of something that is greater than himself."

Frank met Sheila and her son, Ellis, the following Saturday at the empty ballpark.

Frank took the boy's plastic glove and traded him for it, replacing it with a refurbished genuine-leather Wilson model. Frank began with the tennis balls, rolling them to the boy and shouting, "Get your fanny down and catch it with your bare hands. You have to learn to catch with your bare hands – the glove is just for protection."

Sheila watched intently, and at the end of practice, Frank gave her two tennis balls.

"Every afternoon, just play catch with him," Frank said. "Use these tennis balls. Make it a game. Every day, see if he can catch more than he did the day before without missing one." He gave Ellis a packet of plain M&Ms.

She thanked him, and the little boy said, "See you next Saturday," and after a pause, said, "Coach." Frank smiled as he watched them leave.

And deep within, Frank Wilcox, finally at peace, heard the whisper of Terry Thompson remind him, "It's all about the boys," but he also heard the unmistakable assurance that came after that.

Everyone who invests in a child makes a difference in tomorrow.

ACKNOWLEDGMENTS

I want to thank my wife, Vicki, who embraced our family's year-round dedication to the Lexington, South Carolina Dixie Youth Baseball organization (1996-2015), and for patiently understanding what it means to say, "This family is interrupted by baseball season."

I want to thank my sons, Andrew, William, Richard, and Matthew, who collectively played 768 regular-season games and attended more than 1,500 practices over eighteen seasons of springtime Dixie Youth Baseball. Their combined record was 479-289. They played on twelve championship teams and nineteen different All-Star teams. Matthew played on a state championship team that played in a Dixie World Series; William played in two state tournaments. Those boys also played fall baseball. A thrill of my life was to coach each of them for a few of their seasons, to practice with them, and to support them on all their teams. None of them played in high school, but they excelled in other ways, including and most importantly, academically.

I want to thank my good friend and fellow coach Jay "Coach Jay" Tompkins, who coached three of my boys in the older major league, made them better boys and ballplayers, and helped Vicki and me shuttle our boys to practices. From 2004–2006, all four of our boys played on four different teams, practicing at four different locations. We relied on help.

I want to thank pastor Don Turner, Don McManus, Dale and Mary Cook, and every member of Round Hill Baptist Church in Lexington, SC. Together, through the Field of Dreams, many boys were loved and served and learned about teamship, encouragement, and baseball fundamentals. Your church's love for community and openhanded approach to ministry and missions forever changed my life and the lives of hundreds of others.

I once said all of my friends in Lexington, South Carolina came either through church or the ballpark, and that is true. To every board member, coach, and umpire serving through Lexington Dixie Baseball, I thank you. It was a joy to walk through two decades of my life with you.

It's important for me to thank Ed Nelson and Ronnie Nix, both formerly with the Statesboro, Georgia, Recreation Department, and to remember the late Terry Thompson in Jesup, Georgia. Those three men taught me so much in a very few years about community service and how to best coach recreational sports. I will never forget them.

In the words of George Herman "Babe" Ruth, "Baseball was, is, and always will be to me the best game in the world."

THE BLEACHER SECTION

Each name or honoree on these pages represents a financial donation to the pre-production costs of this book. Independent publishing requires authors go it alone in funding the publication costs of their projects. I am so thankful for the names on this page, and the families and friends behind each of them. ~ Scott

Nathan Bottoms and Matthew Bottoms
Tom Cox
In honor of Gerald Blackburn
The Harper Family
Elliot Lance
In memory of Carlton and Pauline Lewis
In honor of Clint Metts
Connor and Trey Mitchell
Bill and Laurie Payne
In memory of Jesse Sainz, IV
Joel and Gina Sauls
The Sumner Family
Jimmy Terrapin & Amy Cofield

THE BLEACHER SECTION

In memory of Eddie Tronco
Mark and Randy West
The Undefeated Shealy Sharks
In memory of Lucille Burruss Phillips
In honor of Tami Whitmire
Joyce Hitt: 1970's baseball coach!
In honor of Johnny Tallant
Luke and Ben Whitmire
In memory of Gayle Brazell
In memory of Edgar Alewine, Sr.
The Byars Family
Reed and Patty Patterson family

ABOUT THE AUTHOR

Scott Douglas Vaughan is a professional writer living in Lexington, South Carolina. Nine Innings is his fifth novel based on stories from his life. His three-book Memories of a Home series, stories of a boy growing up in the '60s and '70s small-town South, won awards in several different national contests. *The Beauty Queen & The Reporter* is an award-winning novella based on how he met his wife, Vicki. Scott is a former award-winning writer in both the Georgia and South Carolina press associations. He is a national public speaker and storyteller, as well as a Sunday-morning Bible teacher. www.scottdvaughan.com

Made in the USA
Columbia, SC
20 May 2021